Spunky

Spunky

by DORI BRINK

SCHOLASTIC BOOK SERVICES
NEW YORK • TORONTO • LONDON • AUCKLAND • SYDNEY • TOKYO

To Paul F. Brink
who makes the impossible possible

Cover photo of Spunky by Elyse Lear

ISBN 0-590-31301-0

12 11 10 9 8 7 6 5 4 3 2   0 1 2 3 4 5/8

Printed in the U.S.A.   06

Prologue

You are asleep now and don't even know I am here watching you. The house is still, and everyone else is asleep too.

I will see that no harm comes to you. If anything happens, I will bark loud and even bite. I've learned a lot in the past year since I was a pup.

As soon as you are able to stretch your legs, we will run through the fields and play together. There is so much I can show you, and so many things we can do.

Strange how much I love you. Up until now I didn't know how love could feel. Maybe if I tell you about myself, you will understand. . . .

1

I lay there shivering in the wet grass. I ate some of it. Then threw up. The knots in my stomach unwound and I crept back inside the paper bag. It crinkled loudly as I crawled far back to the rounded corners and curled myself into a ball. It was all the protection I had from the night.

A bird screeched by above me, and in the distance a wild howling rose into the air. I longed for my mother's warm body and tender lapping. I could still taste the sweetness of her milk and feel the rhythmic rippling of her contented sighs when I pressed against her.

Where was my mother? I wanted her. In

the morning, when the sun came up, I would look for her. The thought of finding her again comforted me and helped me fall asleep.

Suddenly a sharp clawing noise at the opening of the bag shocked me awake. Huge shiny eyes were peering straight at me, and rasping breath filled the bag with foul air. I yelped and thrashed about in my corner until the eyes and mouth withdrew. I dared not sleep again. I listened carefully to the sounds of the night, hoping they would not come closer.

My eyelids drooped, and in my mind I saw again that large hand slowly reaching toward me as I pressed farther back into my mother's softness. I tried to snap at the hand, but it grasped the back of my neck and lifted me up. It dropped me into the bag and carried me out of the house my mother and I had lived in.

At first, there were other pups in the house besides myself. But they had been given away, one by one, to the grown-ups and children who came to look at us. Every time one of them tried to touch me, I snapped at them as hard as I could.

"Mean pup! Nasty little pup!" they would

say, and turn their attention to the others. Then I would settle back under the soft curve of my mother's neck. Soon all the other pups were gone, and I had my mother all to myself.

The hand snapped a rubber band around the top of the bag and there was no way for me to get out. But there was a small opening near the top, letting air through to me.

A car door clicked open and I felt a hard seat beneath me. The motor started and I could feel its vibration through the seat.

The ride was terrifying and long. At last the car came to a halt. I could sense the great distance that now separated me from my mother. The bag was lifted up and the rubber band snapped off. Then the bag and I sailed into the air. I felt a dizzy moment of space, then I thumped to the ground. The car roared away and I listened to the sound fade until all I could hear were the crickets in the grass around me. Through the opening of the bag I could smell the pungent night air.

I looked out into the darkness. Would morning never come? Would it ever come? I could hear my heart beating. The sound blended with the strange rustlings and croakings of the night.

Somehow I dozed again. When I opened my eyes, the sun was there. I crawled out of the bag and stretched my legs. It felt good. I was warm. The fields seemed friendly now and full of light. I could not wait to find my mother. I sniffed about anxiously, but there was no trace of her anywhere. My stomach was in knots again, and I gulped back thick saliva. The thought of her warm milk made the saliva flow more freely down my throat.

Which way should I go? Tall, thick weeds and tangled bushes blocked my view. A string of birds flew by above me, and I lifted my head to watch them. They were heading toward the mountains that jutted into the sky at the far stretches of the field.

A familiar sound caught my ear, and I cocked my head to one side to listen. It was a very faint sound, but I had heard it before. Laughter. Children's laughter. Now there was something to guide me. I headed toward the sound.

2

I could see the children now. They were running about, doing all kinds of things. Some were scrambling after a ball and tossing it into the air when they caught it. Some were sitting on wooden planks, pushing themselves up and down. Others were climbing metal bars, twisting themselves in and out of the openings.

Behind them was a tall brick building surrounded by carpeted grass and smooth pathways. The neatness contrasted sharply with the ragged fields I had been running through.

One of the children caught my eye and

held my attention. He was chewing something. I gulped with anticipation. There was food here. I headed toward him and saw him take a bite from something wrapped in paper. Then a bell clanged and he began to walk toward the building.

I trailed behind the boy, watching him take another bite, then crumple the paper and throw it away. I went after the paper. With my nose I managed to uncrumple it a bit. There was a lick of something sweet inside, a trace of chocolate, so sweet, so tantalizingly delicious, it made me even hungrier than before. And I was thirsty.

The children were all inside the building now. I moved along the smooth pavement, searching for something to eat or drink. A small blob of chewed gum caught my eye. I peeled it from the pavement with my teeth and chewed it in back of my mouth. It did not dissolve, and after a while I just gulped it down my throat. Half a peanut was my next find. That was good. A lollipop covered with ants was my next treat. Now I was more thirsty than hungry.

The pavement around the school building led onto a wide street with rows of houses on either side. The rich aroma of sizzling food came through open windows. Saliva filled my mouth and hunger gripped my insides.

A thin stream of water crossed the pavement. It was coming from a long hose nestled in the grass in front of a house. I licked the stream gratefully, then followed it to the side of the house, where the hose was attached. The water oozed in spurts and I drank my fill.

I felt much better. I could find things to eat and drink. But I had to find much more to fill my stomach. Much more.

I continued along the pavement, keeping my nose close to the ground, sniffing for food. A flutter of wings caught my eye. Birds were settling down near a house I was approaching. They were gathered on the lawn, pecking away at something. I drew closer. Chunks of bread! Crisp bread. I galloped through the cluster of birds and they rose into the air. I snatched the pieces of bread into my mouth as fast as I could.

Heavy footsteps pounded down the pavement at the side of the house, and a huge woman lurched toward me, swinging a broom back and forth.

"Get away from here, you muddy pup!" she shouted. Mounds of fat shivered along her arms as she waved the broom.

I trotted past her to the back of the house, glancing around every few steps. The woman was taking more bread out of her pocket and breaking it into small pieces, letting them drop to the grass. The birds were already back to pick them up.

When I rounded the corner of the house, I almost bumped into a tall garbage can. Crouched on top of the can was a cat, daintily chewing away at a mound of food! I yelped at this incredible sight. Instantly the cat hunched her back and leaped off the can, tipping it over as she jumped.

I drew a quick breath as the wonders of the can were spread out on the ground before me. Peas and carrots wetted with tomato ketchup; squashed peaches; lumps of potatoes topped with waxy fat and paper towels; egg shells with traces of yolk still inside the broken pieces.

Half-hidden by potato peels and coffee grounds was a big juicy bone with fatty meat clinging to it! I had it between my teeth, just as that huge woman loomed over me again.

I jumped aside and the broom whooshed past me. "Get out of here!" the woman screamed and came after me again. This time the broom landed on my backside, pricking my skin. I growled at her as best I could with the bone between my teeth.

She kept swinging that broom at me while I moved away, but the bone was secure in my mouth. Why would she deny me this feast?

A short distance away I paused to look back. The woman was shoveling that wonderful food back into the can. Then she pressed a lid tightly over it. With rolling satisfaction, she pumped herself down the pathway and into the house.

I sank down on the grass with my bone. First I ate the meat, then I scraped and chewed all the tasty grizzle clinging to the surface. Finally I licked and gnawed away at the core until all the juices and gritty marrow were gone. When the bone was completely dry, I rested my chin over it with deep affection. What a wonderful treat.

There must be more treasures like this to be found. I would have to be careful of people, though. They could hurt you so easily.

3

I wandered up and down the rows of houses, checking the garbage cans behind each one. Almost all of them had lids on them. But scraps of food could usually be found nearby if I sniffed around long enough.

Abruptly the streets ended, and the wild fields began again. I was back where I started. I could see the towering mountains in the distance. A huge truck was rolling through the fields, pushing bushes and tangled grass out of its path. It left flat, smooth tracks of earth behind its wheels. The sight fascinated me for a while, but the smell of food coming from the houses made me turn back.

The sun was going down and darkness was settling over the streets. Lights flickered on inside the houses, throwing bushes and pavement into sharp angles and jagged edges. I needed a place to sleep.

I heard the distant howling of animals prowling the fields, and I shuddered at the sounds, remembering my fearful sleep the night before.

In back of one of the houses a garage door was partly open. The acrid smells made me sneeze, but a large, round tire lying in one corner looked inviting. I jumped into its hollow middle and curled myself into a ball. I felt snug and warm. The howling of strange animals would not bother me here.

I licked my whiskers for traces of meat, and sighed. If only my mother were here to cuddle up against. My mother. It was the first time since morning that I had thought of her. With the taste of meat still clinging to my whiskers, the memory of her sweet milk was fading away.

Each day I searched for food and got better and better at finding it. Constant hunger sharpened my alertness. Within a week I knew exactly where to go and at what time of day.

I discovered that children liked me. And children often had something sweet to eat in their hands. At the brick school building, when the sun was sitting straight up in the sky, they all came outside to play.

Each day at that time I was there, waiting for them. I watched for children holding a piece of candy or cake, and wagged my way over to them. While they fussed over me and stroked my shaggy hair with sticky fingers, I made the grab. Shrill cries followed me when I ran off with the sweet treasure. But the children always welcomed me back again the next day.

When the sun went down, I went from house to house sniffing around the garbage cans. People usually loaded them after their evening meal, and I could find delicious scraps of food that had landed on the ground. I wished I could get inside those cans, and I kept an eye out for another cat to tip one over for me.

Once I did find another cat perched on top of a can. But when I barked as loud as I could to frighten it into action, the cat only hissed and spat at me.

Hardest to bear were the dusty, indifferent men who came down the streets regularly to take the cans away. A huge truck with an enormous appetite followed them everywhere. I ran after the men, yapping at their heels, begging them not to take the cans. But they paid no attention to me. One by one they carried the cans to the truck, and emptied them into its huge, ever-chomping mouth.

One night I had slept under the back stairs of a house because the doors of my garage were shut. In the morning, mingling with the sun-baked wood of the stairs and the fresh paint of the house, came the smell of eggs frying and bacon sizzling. I traced the agonizing whiffs to a nearby window and sat there, shifting with longing.

Suddenly the door at the top of the stairs swung open and a woman came out holding a bowl in her hands. She shielded her eyes from the sun and called, "Here, kitty, kitty. . ." Finally, with an impatient shrug, she put the bowl down and went back inside the house.

The moment the door closed a cat crept out of the bushes near the house. After making sure I hadn't moved, it quickly ran up the stairs to the bowl. It was lapping milk into its mouth, squeezing its eyes with pleasure.

I moved slowly, and when I was right under the stairs I barked! The cat jumped off the landing and darted away. The next moment *I* was drinking milk. Cool, sweet, delicious milk!

I was under those stairs the following morning, waiting to see if another miracle would happen. It did. As soon as the woman went back inside, I was at the bowl, lapping away with pleasure. The cat kept her distance, although I could hear her cry not too far away.

As my self-reliance grew, my spirits soared. After a particularly good find, I would feel playful and run about in zigzags to express my joy. Sometimes I rolled on the grass in ecstasy, with the bright sun smiling down at me.

One afternoon I saw a dog bounding out of one of the houses in fitful strides. Attached to his neck was a long, thin leash, held tightly by the man behind him. I could see the dog wanted to run, but the man held him back. I ran up to the dog and sniffed his nose. The man pulled the leash up sharply, yanking the dog away from me. But the dog pulled and thrashed toward me until his eyes bulged with frustration.

I could not help showing off my freedom. I ran about in circles in front of him, then darted up and across his lawn and down his very own steps. Giddy with joy, I ran across the street then dashed back again to the dog. I smiled up into his tortured face. The man finally dragged the dog away from me. I watched them go with great pity. How sad to be tied like that to a man.

I had no way of knowing during this time that rain would come and ruin all my sources of food and shelter. I had never known rain before. The first drops were like pellets hitting me, and I looked up to the sky in surprise. Huge, dark clouds were moving menacingly above me. Thunder cracked in my ears and flashes of light scorched my eyes. Children ran through the streets, shrieking happily when they reached their houses.

For a moment, I didn't know where to go. Then I remembered. I ran for the garage. The door was open, but rain splashed through the roof, making puddles of water everywhere. Even the rubber tire was damp and cold. I shivered, and wondered how long I would have to bear it.

The rain was to last for days. The mornings were gray. No bowl of milk was left outside. I watched the cat being let into the warmly lit house. The scraps around the garbage cans were soggy and tasteless, and the school children did not play outside.

One evening, I sat under an awning at the back of one of the houses. The rain streamed down just a few inches in front of my nose, and soft light shone through the glass door.

I looked inside. People were passing platters of steaming meat and vegetables to each other around a table. I saw a familiar head bob up alongside the table. It was the dog I had seen on the leash a few days ago. He was sitting beside the man who had yanked him away from me.

The dog touched the man's arm with his paw, and the man turned and tossed him a piece of meat. The dog caught it expertly, gobbling it down with keen pleasure. I gulped in anguish. Another delicious sliver of meat was thrown and caught. Now the man swirled a piece of bread into a bowl of gravy and the dog licked it out of his hand. It was too much for me.

I plodded back to the garage through the soggy grass, stunned by what I had seen. Inside my cold tire, I thought about that dog. Just a few days ago I had pitied him. Now, more than anything else, I wanted to be inside a warmly lit house, being fed wonderful things to eat.

But only people lived in houses. I would have to find someone to live with. Until now I had avoided people, aware of the pain they could cause. I sighed deeply, wishing the rain would stop.

4

A few days later, trusting only my instincts, I chose Peter. I found him unexpectedly.

Very early in the morning, the sound of hammering awakened me. I shook myself and went outside the garage. The rain had stopped, although a chilly wetness clung to everything. The hammering was coming from the fields, where the land had been cleared. Drifting through the air, from the direction of the hammering, came the pungent smell of coffee. My hunger was an ache inside me, and the chance of finding food made me wild with hope. I ran as fast as I could.

Parked on the road, near the cleared field, was a food wagon. Workmen were gathered around it, eating and drinking. On the open side of the wagon, piled high on a counter, were layers of sandwiches, rolls, and cakes. Steaming coffee was being poured into cups and handed to the men. I almost choked at the sight of it all. How could I get some?

I edged in between their feet, trying not to be stepped on. They were talking and laughing. No one noticed me. I barked up at one of the men, shifting my paws and tossing my head for emphasis. He looked down at me and smiled, then tore off a piece of bread from his sandwich and threw it to me.

I caught it mid-air, and gobbled it down.

"Hey. That's cute!" he said.

Another man looked down. He threw me a piece of cake. Then another man, and another. Soon they were all tossing pieces of bread and cake into the air. I chased after each piece, gulping it down while frantically going after the next piece.

They were all laughing now.

One of the men dangled a whole dough-nut high above my head.

"Jump! Jump!" he shouted.

I leaped up and tried to grab it. But the man pulled his hand away just as I snapped my jaws together. My teeth sank into his fleshy thumb.

"Ouch," he cried. His face was twisted with pain and anger. With a fierce motion, he kicked me in the ribs. I yelped at the pain, then snapped at his leg. He yelled and came after me, but I swirled around in back of him and caught his trousers between my teeth. I pulled and pulled, trying to tear them apart. The man floundered off-balance, dancing on one foot.

The other men gathered around us, laughing and shouting. I didn't loosen my grip, even when the man struck my nose.

"What's this, a karate match?" A forceful voice penetrated the commotion, and suddenly all the laughing and shouting stopped. The man I had been struggling with slackened his dance, and I dropped my jaws. He stepped back.

"Ah, just having a little fun with this mutt," he said, shuffling his feet.

I looked up at the man who had made everything stop. It was the first time I saw Peter. His face was set into firm lines, but the eyes looking down at me had a kind, soft light in them. A wave of tenderness came over me, and I felt I was breathing in his kindness.

20

He knelt down and stroked my ear. His touch was gentle. All at once I knew that he was someone I could live with. How could I tell him?

Peter straightened up and said to the others, "Okay. Fun's over. So's the coffee break."

The men broke into loud talk and laughter again as they moved toward a row of skeleton houses going up alongside the road. I followed behind Peter. Now and then he stopped to examine the wooden frames being nailed together. Then he walked down the road to his trailer. I was right behind him. He opened the door and quickly went inside, shutting me out. Why was he trying to get away from me?

I sprawled down on the step in front of the door listening to the sound of his movements inside. A phone rang, and I heard the faint murmur of his soothing voice. It lulled me into a peaceful sleep.

5

Footsteps awakened me. Peter was coming outside again. I scrambled to my feet and quickly followed him.

He got into his car and drove back to the work site. I chased after him. When he got out to talk with the workmen, I sprawled on my belly, resting my chin on my front paws. I waited until he walked on. Sometimes he inspected the work closely. Other times he stopped only long enough to make a man laugh with a few words, or clap someone on the back without losing stride. Whatever his pace, I kept up with him.

One time he stopped near a group of men piling up long planks of wood lying on the ground. He took a pencil out of his pocket and huddled over a huge piece of paper with one of the workmen. I knew it would be a long wait. I sat down in the middle of a plank two workmen were about to lift up. They tried to get me off, but I ran back and forth out of their reach. It was fun.

"Hey Peter, you better take your dog away," one of the workmen called, trying to grab me.

"That's *not* my dog," Peter said, walking toward me. I jumped off the plank and ran to meet Peter, smiling up at him. He turned away.

He moved on to another group of men pouring soft cement into a hole in the ground. They smoothed it very carefully and it looked shiny and inviting. I padded across it. Peter scooped me up into his arms, and carried me back to his car.

"Stay here!" he commanded and shut the door. I liked being in Peter's car and settled down to sleep.

When Peter let me out, it was growing dark. I was ready to walk along with him, but he quickly went to the other side of the car and got in, closing the door before I reached it. Then he roared away from me.

I ran with all my might. At the trailer, he stopped the car and got out. Panting and breathless, I managed to slip by the door just as he opened it.

Peter shook his head and looked down at me, then went to the water cooler and filled a cup. He put it on the floor.

"That's for you," he said. I drank greedily.

Peter packed some papers into a case and snapped it shut, put on his jacket, and slipped his cigarettes into a pocket. Standing beside the desk, he picked up the phone and made it buzz.

"Hi, Daphne. What's good?" His voice was especially soft and friendly, different from the way it sounded when he talked to anyone else during the day.

". . . Yeah? Okay . . . I'll be home in a little while. I'm leaving now. Okay, Daphne. Bye."

Peter strode to the door and I kept close to his heels, ready to leave with him.

With one hand on the doorknob, he looked down at me.

"You stay here tonight," he said firmly,

then knelt down and gently pushed me back. He went outside, closing the door behind him.

It soon grew dark inside the trailer, but his chair and desk were there, and I could sniff traces of his footsteps on the floor, and beside the wastebasket a paper towel he had used to dry his hands. These things comforted me. The cup of water gleamed at me from the floor. I settled down under Peter's desk to sleep.

Early the next morning I heard his car door slam. With a burst of sunlight the trailer door opened. I jumped up at Peter's legs, then ran in wild circles around him. I did a somersault, then rolled on my back, pawing the air in ecstasy.

Peter knelt down and smiled. Deep crinkles appeared around his eyes. His gentle touch played with my ears. I stared into his face intently. How could I tell him what I wanted?

Soon men came into the trailer, asking questions and rattling papers. The phone rang. More men came in. Through the open door came a whiff of the food wagon. I went outside. I was very hungry.

Workmen were already gathering around

the wagon, eating and drinking. I sat down on the foot of one of the men. He looked down and chuckled, then tossed me a piece of roll. Soon the other men were tossing pieces of cake and bread into the air for me to catch. I scrambled after every piece.

Then the man who had kicked me the day before stood in front of me. He dangled a fat piece of doughnut over my head.

"Jump!" he said harshly. I steadied my legs and growled up at him.

"Come on, jump!" he repeated. A snarl rose deep within my throat and I bared my teeth.

"Ain't that something!" someone said.

"Gutsy little pup!" said another.

I held my ground until the man lowered his hand and shuffled away from the crowd of men around the wagon.

Through all the commotion, I heard Peter's voice. He was drinking coffee and talking quietly with one of the men. I went over to him and he looked down at me. A smile played around his lips. Then suddenly his eyebrows drew together and his face settled into a frown. He turned his head away. The other men were all around me now, watching curiously.

"Where do you suppose he came from?" one of them asked.

"Beats me. There are more stray dogs in these parts than you can shake a stick at."

"Looks to me like he's half-sheepdog and half-terrier."

"He's a terror all right!" Laughter.

"Cute though. Too bad he's got no one to take care of him."

"Looks to me like he can take care of himself."

More laughter. Not from Peter. He wasn't smiling, and his eyebrows seemed to be even more closely drawn together. But at least he was looking at me again.

He put his cup down, shrugged his shoulders back as if he were trying to shake something loose, and walked briskly away. I followed him. He glanced back at me, and walked faster.

When he reached his car, he jumped into it and roared down the road. I chased after the wheels, running with all my might through the dust and fumes. A short distance away, he stopped and got out. I was right there to greet him, wagging my tail triumphantly. He just stood there frowning and scratching his head.

"What in the world am I going to do with you?" he muttered. I smiled up at him, but he turned away.

For several days, it was the same. At night Peter let me sleep in his trailer, but during the day, more and more often, he jumped into his car and roared away from me.

So one afternoon when he did this, instead of chasing after him, I went to his trailer. Sooner or later I knew he would return. I sprawled down on the step in front of the door and rested my paws on my chin. It was a long wait. When he finally drove up and got out of his car, he just walked over to where I was lying and glared down at me with his hands on his hips. I sat up and scratched my ear, pretending not to notice he was there.

Suddenly he laughed, and I looked up at him. All the deep crinkles in his face were showing.

"You're just about as smart as they come, aren't you!" he said.

He held the door of his trailer wide open for me, then went straight to the phone. He spoke in that special friendly voice.

"Hi, Daphne. How would you like a dog?

. . . A dog . . . Yeah, I know we're not allowed to have dogs in the apartment, but we'll be out of there in a couple of weeks. . . . What? . . . He's black and white . . . shaggy . . . long, curly hair . . . big brown eyes. . . . Okay, I'll bring him home tonight. Bye. Hey! His name's Spunky. . . . Yeah, Spunky. Bye."

6

When Peter shut the door of his trailer that evening, I was outside with him.

"We're going home!" he said. I looked up at him carefully. There was no frown on his face. I jumped up at his legs and wagged my tail joyfully. Peter was taking me home.

I sat close beside him in the car, and from time to time I turned to meet his smile with my own.

At last we stopped in front of a building with rows of windows in it. I followed Peter up a flight of stairs, and he opened a door with his key.

As soon as we entered, a woman came toward us. She stopped in front of me, her legs planted wide apart. She was tall and slim. Long dark hair curved around one side of her neck and fell down in sparkling waves as she leaned forward. Her dancing eyes seemed to catch the light of a nearby lamp.

I wagged my tail nervously.

"Say hello to Daphne, Spunk!" Peter said.

"Black and white!" she exclaimed "I can hardly see the white!"

"Well," said Peter, "he needs a little cleaning up."

She laughed and scooped me off the floor.

"Into the tub you go."

She carried me into a small room and promptly turned on a streaming thunder of water that made vicious whirlpools inside the tub. I tried desperately not to let her put me into this horror. I wriggled and yelped, but her hands held me firmly. Water and sweet smelling soap were poured over me and I was scrubbed from head to foot with foaming bubbles.

I nipped her hand.

"Ouch!" she cried. "You stop that!"

Her hands moved swiftly, and I did my best to nip her again. I succeeded once or twice, but she didn't stop.

At last I was lifted out and smothered in a huge towel. She rubbed me briskly. Then I was released.

I shook the water out of my ears and heard her cry out. I ran through the apartment, rubbing myself into anything I could find. The air was chilly. In one room there was a bed, with frilly material covering its sides. I rubbed myself against it gratefully. Then I heard her footsteps coming after me. Quickly, I crawled underneath the bed. Part of the frilly material was lifted up and I saw her face peering at me sideways. I backed into the farthest corner.

"Come on out, Spunky. The bath's over."

I didn't move.

"Don't you want some dinner?" Her voice was lilting. But when I wouldn't come out, she sighed impatiently, and the frill dropped back into place. I heard her leave the room. In the dim light under the bed I could make out a familiar object: Peter's shoes. I curled myself on top of them and sulked.

All I had wanted was to be with Peter in a cozy home, where he would toss me wonderful things to eat, where he would stroke me and make me feel warm inside. Instead I was trapped in a place where a strange woman could scoop me up and shock me with chilling wetness. The bitter taste of disappointment settled on my tongue.

Soon the smell of food drifted into the room. I heard the sound of plates rattling and I knew they were eating.

I crept out from under the bed and cautiously followed the mouth-watering aroma into the kitchen. They were seated at a table. Peter was putting a forkful of meat into his mouth.

"Oh, there you are, Spunk," he said.

Daphne turned her head and a look of wonder came into her eyes. "He really *is* black and white!"

She got up quickly and took a bowl out of the cupboard. I watched intently as she poured milk into it, then cracked open an egg and plopped it into the milk. She stirred the mixture together and placed the bowl on the floor. I lapped it up greedily. Delicious.

Still licking my whiskers, I sat down next to Peter's feet and watched him eat. I stared hard at every mouthful of food he chewed until he shifted in his chair and threw me a sliver of meat. Incredibly delicious.

"Don't give him anything, Peter. He has to learn good manners," Daphne said.

"A little piece of meat won't hurt him." Peter let me eat another piece right out of his hand.

This was more like it.

Early the next morning, I awoke with a start and jumped off the soft armchair I had cuddled into during the night. Peter was at the door, saying good-bye to Daphne. I ran to him, anxious to leave the house. I wagged my tail happily, waiting for the door to open so I could run down the stairs with Peter.

But he gently pushed me away from the opening.

"You stay here with Daphne," he said. A feeling of dread came over me.

He smiled at Daphne. "Make sure Mrs. Baxter doesn't see him."

"Don't worry," she replied. "I won't take him out during the day. I'll do my shopping tonight. She's not likely to see us after dark."

"Good," Peter said and patted me on the head. He closed the door behind him, and I listened to his footsteps fade away.

I was alone with Daphne. Trapped.

Sure enough, she scooped me up and carried me into the kitchen. She spread a pile of newspapers around one corner of the room and set me down on top of them.

"Stay!" she commanded, pointing her finger at me, her legs wide apart. I darted between her legs and ran into the living room. I squatted down and wet the rug.

Screams: "No! No!"

She grabbed me and carried me back to the pile of newspapers.

"Do it there!" she commanded, towering over me, one hand on her hip, the other pointing to the newspaper.

I waited. Hunger was rippling inside me. I wanted to eat, to chew something. She mixed egg and milk into a bowl and for a few moments I tasted delight.

Later that afternoon, I sulked on my pile of newspapers, listening to the sounds Daphne was making at the sink. The feeling of being trapped churned inside me. I longed to run in the fields and roam the streets, to be free to do whatever I pleased, no one to scream at me and hold me back.

As soon as she left the room, I darted out again. I crawled underneath a table and began to sharpen my teeth against the wood.

"Come out of there!" she cried. She had to crawl down on her hands and knees to reach me. Back we went to the newspaper.

This time when her back was turned, I ran to the bedroom and tested my teeth on some low-hanging curtains. They began to shred easily.

More screams.

When she brought me back, I stood rigidly on top of the paper. She pressed my back down with her hand until my hind legs bent underneath me.

"Sit," she said. I knew how to sit. What did she want from me?

Daphne began to rub spicy scents into meat and cut up vegetables. My mouth watered. Soon the smells of roast pork filled the room. I sighed and sprawled flat on my belly, breathing in the aroma of the sizzling meat. I closed my eyes and thought of the slivers Peter would give me at dinnertime.

Would it taste as good as the scraps I had found when I was free? No, it would be much, much better than anything I had ever tasted before. Still, I longed to be running about, and resentment soured my mouth. One of these days, I promised myself, I would find a way to escape from Daphne. I would run as far away as I could go. With visions of myself galloping through fields, I dozed until Peter came home.

After dinner that night, Daphne put the collar around my neck and clipped the leash onto it. Peter had proudly brought these home with him, so I didn't struggle when she put them on. But a sinking feeling found its way to the pit of my stomach. Now she would lead me around wherever she pleased.

"Be back in a little while," she called out. Peter was in another room, busily working on some papers.

"Don't let Mrs. Baxter catch you," he called back cheerfully.

"Oh, she's probably in bed by now. Besides, Spunky needs the exercise."

Daphne opened the door and hurried down the stairs. There was a blob of chewing gum, a candy wrapper, and other interesting tidbits in the nooks and corners of the stairs. Each time I strained to get at them, she yanked me back. The collar tore into my neck.

"Walk nicely!" she commanded.

I tugged and tugged. She pulled harder. Outside on the street, I wanted to stop and examine everything we passed. She wouldn't let me. How could I ever get free? Now I was something I had once pitied, a dog tied to a leash.

People passing by smiled at us.

"That's a little bit of heaven," one woman said, stopping to pat my head. Daphne smiled down at me, but her hold on my collar never eased. I couldn't follow the curious woman.

We approached a huge building with doors that swung open for us all by themselves. As soon as we were inside, so many food smells hit my nostrils at once that I tugged at the leash frantically. I wanted to taste every single one of them.

A man walked up to us.

"Sorry, miss. No dogs allowed in the store."

Daphne led me outside again. Near the swinging doors, she found a pole and tied the leash around it.

After she made sure it was secure, she stood over me and pointed her finger at my nose.

"Stay," she commanded. I rose up on my

hind legs and pawed the air. I could not pull loose.

She walked away, into the store. I was alone in front of a bewildering place, where people walked in and out, passing me by. Some stopped to smile at me or pat my head, but no one released me no matter how loud I barked.

Daphne came out of the store carrying a large grocery bag. It was a relief to be freed from the pole at last. We started back along the same streets we had taken before.

When we came to the door leading upstairs to the apartment, Daphne gasped. A heavy-set woman with her hands on her hips stood in front of us, blocking the way.

"Is that your dog?" The woman's voice was shrill and accusing.

"Yes, Mrs. Baxter." Daphne was fidgeting with the leash. She added quickly, "It's only for a couple of weeks until we move. He won't be any trouble."

"There are no dogs allowed in this building!"

"Yes, but — "

The leash slipped out of Daphne's hands, and I wriggled over to the woman and sniffed the hem of her skirt. Then I raised my head and looked straight into her eyes. The stiffness in her body melted. She bent down and patted my head. I smiled.

"He's a cutie," she muttered under her breath.

Daphne quickly nodded her head. "He's very good. He's housebroken already!"

That was a lie. I could still hear her screams of No! No! echoing in my head each time I had gone near the rug that day.

"Well, make sure he doesn't dirty up the place."

"Oh, he won't," said Daphne happily. We ran up the steps and into the apartment.

"Whew!" Daphne said, and plumped into a low chair. She reached out and grabbed me up into her lap.

"Give me a kiss!" she demanded.

She took hold of the tufts of hair under my chin and brought my face close to hers. Then she kissed me on the nose.

"Kiss!" she said. Dim memories came back to me of my mother's tender lapping; the snug warmth I felt when I cuddled under her neck; the way I had returned her kisses with my own. Now I had no desire to kiss anyone. I jumped off Daphne's lap. It made her angry.

She crouched down on the floor and screwed her face up. I growled at her. She growled back and jabbed at me with one hand. It was all I needed. I lunged at her, biting her wherever my teeth could land.

"Ouch!" she cried, covering her head with both arms and rolling over on the floor. I came at her again with all my force. She cuffed me on the side of the mouth, and sat up.

"No biting!" she said sternly. "And no more wetting the rug!" I glared up at her, snarling.

Her face softened. "Boy, Spunk, you're mean." She said this with unexpected tenderness, and stroked my ears. I stopped snarling.

7

By mid-afternoon of the next day, Daphne had grown tired of chasing after me. She put me back on the newspapers after another sudden rush to the rug, and sighed deeply. Slowly she returned to the dishes she had been washing. Her arms sagged to her sides and she leaned back against the sink.

Then her eyes lit up as she looked at me with a sudden thought. "Come with me," she said. I followed her.

She walked to the door with slow, deliberate steps and opened it.

"Look, Spunky," she pleaded, "when you want to go outside, say *Woof, Woof*." The sound she made was very much like my own.

"See," she said, closing and opening the door again. "Outside."

I knew what outside was. I pulled one corner of my mouth into a side grimace and looked at her patiently. Would she really take me out if I barked? Could it be as easy as all that? I had my doubts.

She closed the door with a final slam, and went back to the kitchen.

I listened to her washing the dishes for a while, then I decided to try it. I went to the door, sat down beside it, and barked.

Daphne came running over to me. "What's that?" she asked, her eyes wide with wonder.

"*Woof, Woof!*" I repeated clearly.

Her mouth opened wide and she did not seem to know where to move first. She grabbed her jacket and my leash and opened the door, trying to pump her arms into the sleeves at the same time.

We ran down the stairs together without stopping once.

Daphne was in a very good mood that night. She was full of laughter during dinner and chatted away brightly even when Peter went into the living room and tried to read his newspaper.

"He really did!" she was saying. "He sat down at the door and barked just the way I told him!"

"Sure, sure," Peter said, raising his eyes to the ceiling the way he had done the last time she told the story.

I settled down beside Peter's chair and watched him tap his foot on the floor in time to Daphne's chatting.

There were many strange things in Peter's home. But the strangest thing of all I discovered in the bedroom one morning.

I wandered into the room, sniffing around the side of the bed where Daphne was sitting. With a laugh, she scooped me into her arms, pressing me against her so that my front paws dangled over her shoulder.

Suddenly, on the dresser facing me, I saw a dog! It had long, silky ears and a round, shiny nose. A spray of hair partly covered its eyes, and shaggy, long, curling hair covered the rest of it. Its ears pricked up when it saw me, and a long, flowing tail waved back and forth. I barked. The dog barked. I wiggled out of Daphne's grasp, bounded across the bed, and up on the dresser. My nose bumped up against a hard, smooth surface. The dog's face was close to me but I could not smell a trace of its scent. The tail was moving back and forth quickly. I barked and it barked.

Daphne laughed.

"Spunky, that's you," she explained.

Me? I was bewildered. What did she mean? I sniffed the hard surface again. Then I peeked behind it. The dog was gone. Only when I looked in front of it did I see the dog again.

Daphne picked me up. Now Daphne was holding the dog and smiling.

"See, Spunky. That's me and that's you."

Now I understood. Daphne could be in two places at one time.

"It's a mirror," she said.

I learned to accept mirrors wherever I found them. In a pool of water in the street, in shiny lamps, metal doors—just about anywhere. Each time I saw the dog again, I pretended not to notice him.

That afternoon, unexpectedly, I got a chance for freedom.

"How would you like to go for a walk in the park?" Daphne asked.

I looked up at her, puzzled. What was a "park"?

She put the leash on me and we went outside. We walked for a long time before reaching a wide fence surrounded by trees. A cobbled pathway led inside. Quiet stretches of grass and tangled bushes lay before us. The farther we walked, the more excited I became. Here were things I knew and understood, birds trilling, leaves rustling, scents of other animals, and earth baking in the sun. I wanted to explore every part of it and tugged frantically.

Daphne bent down and took off my leash. I was free! For a moment, I was startled. I buried my nose in all the strange new scents, trying to identify them. I retraced each enticing path, getting deeper and deeper into the bushes.

I could hear Daphne calling me, but I had no intention of going back to her. I went on and on, zigzagging in and out of every bush I found.

There was a clearing in front of me. A bird was sitting on a rippling surface, flapping its wings but not flying away. I moved closer to it, entranced. It seemed to glide farther away. I ran after it. Suddenly the ground dissolved underneath me. Water poured into my ears and mouth. For a moment I couldn't breathe. I struggled desperately to find solid ground. Then hands clutched me and swept me into the air. Daphne was carrying me in her arms.

She set me down on the cobbled pathway. I shook the water out of my ears and body. Then I heard the leash being clipped onto my collar, and Daphne was pulling me. I held back, trying with all my strength to free myself again.

She pulled harder.

"Come on," she said harshly. "We're going home!" She pulled and pulled and managed to drag me out of the park.

My freedom was short-lived.

On Saturday, without warning, Daphne put me in Peter's car and announced that we were going to see the "nice doctor."

As soon as we entered the waiting room, the harsh smell of medicine hit my nostrils. I could hear the faint sounds of animals whining with fright somewhere behind the walls.

Daphne sat down and picked up a magazine. I ran to the door leading outside. She picked me up and put me in her lap.

"Be good," she said. "The nice doctor won't hurt you."

I shivered. A woman in a white coat motioned for us to follow her.

The doctor was standing behind a high table with a bright light over it. Daphne put me on top of the table, murmuring soothings words to me and stroking my ears. I scrambled to jump off. The doctor firmly held me back. His touch was not unkind. I relaxed a little.

His hands probed all over me. My eyes, nose, ears, stomach, and back. He used a wooden stick to look at my tongue and throat.

Finally, Daphne asked, "Is he healthy, doctor?"

"Oh, yes, *she's* very healthy."

"Oh," said Daphne with an embarrassed laugh. "I always call dogs 'he.'"

The doctor smiled while concentrating on a long needle he was filling with fluid. "Well, he's a she, all right."

The color in Daphne's face deepened. "My husband also calls dogs 'he' without thinking. Just a habit," she added quickly.

"Judging from her teeth," said the doctor frowning at the needle, "I would say she's about three months old. This rabies shot is none too soon."

I shifted my paws and kept an eye on the doctor's hands. One of them now pointed the needle at me; the other reached for the back of my neck. I yelped. In the needle went. I didn't actually feel pain. Still, I looked at the door longingly. In a moment, my neck was released.

Daphne lifted me off the table and put me on the floor. I scrambled to the door and sat down, barking impatiently. They were smiling at me.

"Spunky's quite a combination," said the doctor. "Part sheep dog, part terrier, and perhaps a little Hungarian puli in her."

"She's one of a kind!" Daphne replied proudly.

The doctor bent down and stroked my head.

"Smart as a whip," he said.

Sitting in the front seat with Daphne, I watched the streets pass as we drove home. A light changed color at a corner and we waited for it to change again.

She leaned toward me, her face tilted to one side.

"Give me a kiss?" she asked.

I stared straight ahead. She repeated her request, this time pleading. I grumbled my impatience and shifted my front paws, without turning my head. I stared at the street light.

The last thing I felt like doing was kissing her, especially after that visit with the doctor. How could I ever escape all the things she made me suffer? The light changed and she continued driving. Out of the corner of my eye, I could tell she was unhappy by the way she pressed her lips together.

8

I felt a certain tension in the conversation at dinner that night. I listened attentively, an uneasy feeling coming over me.

"Dodger will make a terrific watchdog," Peter was saying. "We'll need one in that place. It's pretty isolated. Right now, anyway."

"Do you think a dog that's five years old can adjust easily? I mean, do you think he'll take to us after living with other people for so long? And, by the way, Peter, is Dodger male or female?" Daphne said all this very quickly.

Peter smiled. "Like the nice doctor said, he's a she."

"Very funny," Daphne replied without smiling, and tapped her nails on the table.

Peter continued talking seriously. "Dodger's living in a kennel now. That's hard on a big Weimaraner. They're natural hunters you know — need lots of space. The people who had her before kept her in a small backyard. Hardly saw the dog during the day. Working people. So Dodger was alone a lot."

"Why did they give her up?"

"Moved to an apartment, and you can't keep a dog like that in an apartment."

A worried pause.

"Can't we wait until we move to the house before picking her up, Peter?"

"I want to take her before the woman who runs the kennel changes her mind. She doesn't want Dodger to suffer being in a kennel a moment longer than necessary. If we don't take the dog right away, she might find someone else. Dodger's a high-strung animal, and prolonged stress might make her sick."

Daphne bit her thumbnail. "Sounds like she's not used to animals or people!"

"Don't worry. She's a very intelligent dog. She'll be all right."

Another worried pause.

"When do you want to pick her up?" Daphne asked.

"Sunday morning. The woman wants to look you over first. I've already passed inspection with flying colors."

"Hah!" Daphne made a fist and jabbed at him lightly.

Peter smiled and took her hand. I could tell he liked her. I wondered why.

All the way to the kennel, I had a feeling of apprehension. There was that same current of tension in their talk.

"What will we do if Mrs. Baxter sees Dodger?" Daphne suddenly asked. "She didn't make too much fuss over Spunky, but if she sees Dodger she'll have a fit."

"Don't worry. We'll be moving in less than a week. I can take Dodger to the job during the day, and at night she can sleep in the car."

Daphne was tugging at her fingers.

"How do you think she and the Spunk will get along?"

I raised my head. I had been resting it in Peter's lap. It was the first time they had given me a serious thought during the whole drive.

"We'll see." It wasn't much of a thought.

I put my head back in Peter's lap. All this tension was making me tired.

The car stopped in front of a low, sprawling building, enclosed by a high metal fence. As soon as the car door clicked open, a herd of dogs crammed against the fence, snarling and barking at us. Peter and Daphne got out and told me to stay. As they walked into the building, the snarls and barks became an uproar, and I was glad the metal fence held all the dogs back.

When Peter and Daphne came out again, they were accompanied by a short, tangle-haired woman. At the end of a leash, tightly clasped to her side, was a huge, wild-eyed dog. As they walked to the car, the dogs behind the fence began to whine. The woman turned and spoke to them in a soothing voice.

"Be good now, Clancy. Susan, stop that noise. Be a little sweetheart now, David. What a love you are."

She ran her hand along the metal fence and some of the dogs managed to lick her fingers through the openings.

Still clutching Dodger to her side, she approached the car. I pressed my nose against the window and watched intently.

The big dog was trembling with fear. Her eyes darted about, first looking at the woman, then at Peter and Daphne. Her mouth was half-parted, exposing enormous teeth. For a few moments, there was an uneasy silence. Then Daphne stepped forward.

"I'll take her," she said. She leaned close to Dodger and lightly stroked her ear. The wildness in Dodger's eyes disappeared and a look of pleading came into them. She searched Daphne's face for kindness.

Holding the leash firmly, Daphne led Dodger into the car. With an awkward stiffness, she climbed onto the back seat. She seemed to fill all the space behind me. Daphne sat beside her, stroking her neck and murmuring soothing words into her ear.

Peter got in beside me and started the motor.

"Don't forget!" the woman called as we drove away. "Only raw meat."

Dodger sat stiffly beside Daphne, eyes darting out of the window, drool oozing out of the corners of her mouth. I settled down to enjoy the ride, now that I had Peter all to myself in the front seat.

Peter parked the car about half a block from our building. When he got out, I jumped out after him. Daphne opened the back door and stepped out of the car hesitantly. Dodger sat upright, rigid with fear.

Daphne ducked her head inside and patted Dodger on the shoulder. "You stay here," she said. Her voice was soothing. She closed the door, sealing Dodger in securely.

We started to walk, then stopped short. A howling from the car was piercing the street like a siren.

"We'll have to take her with us," Peter said quickly. He hurried back to the car and opened the back door. Dodger came bounding out.

We all rushed up the stairs together, bumping into each other. "Nobody saw us," Daphne whispered to Peter at the landing.

Inside the apartment, the air seemed charged with electric currents. Dodger made everything seem small. She prowled around the rooms, stiff-legged, sniffing everywhere. Peter sat down in his armchair in the living room and watched her. I seated myself on the floor beside Peter and watched too. Daphne went into the kitchen, and the dishes seemed to clatter more loudly than usual.

At last we were called in to eat. There beside my bowl on the floor was a giant one — filled with ground raw meat. My bowl had its usual nuggets, topped with strips of chicken and gravy.

My appetite was good, but out of the corner of my eye, I watched Dodger. Slowly the mound of meat was disappearing. Her eyes were narrowed with pleasure.

She finished before I did, and moved away. Immediately I left my food to inspect her bowl. A few traces of meat clung to the sides of the dish and I licked them up. Dodger was watching me. Did she mind? I paused to look at her, a little frightened at the thought of her disapproval. No. She lowered her gaze. It was all right. Now she was inspecting my dish. I felt a moment's panic, but she snorted and turned away from the food. I rushed over to finish my meal before she could change her mind.

Peter and Daphne took their coffee into the living room, and I quickly followed them. So did Dodger. When Peter sat down in his armchair, I jumped into his lap. This way I was higher than Dodger. When she sat down next to Peter's chair, I stretched my neck as high as I could. I was at least a head above her. Peter stroked her gently, but the restless eyes kept darting around the room.

I wanted Peter to stroke me too. I nudged his free hand, but he was totally absorbed in Dodger and didn't respond. I nudged again. No response. I nipped his hand. Instantly Dodger had my ear between her teeth. I yelped.

She had only pressed my ear slightly, and all I had felt was a sting of pain, but I realized she could have bitten my ear off. Dodger was looking directly at me now. Her eyes were angry. I whimpered my hurt at her. All I had done was nip Peter's hand. But suddenly I knew this was exactly what Dodger was forbidding me to do again. I sank down into Peter's lap and lowered my head.

What a spot to be in. Didn't I have enough trouble with Daphne? Now I had big Dodger telling me what not to do.

Peter left for work early next morning and took Dodger with him.

"I'll sneak her back into the apartment tonight when it's dark," he told Daphne before he left.

I wanted to go with Peter too, but Daphne held me back from the door. I watched Dodger's short tail twitch nervously as she hobbled down the stairs with Peter, but I envied her just the same.

Daphne closed the door behind them, and once again I was at her command.

Something new was added to her attempts to get me to obey her sit-and-stay orders. With each command, she held a bone-shaped biscuit in her hand and only gave it to me after I did as she said. It was a delicious, satisfying thing to chew, and I relished it.

This time she sat down in a low chair and dangled one of these biscuits above her lap.

"Come on, Spunk," she said, patting her lap with her free hand. "Up!"

I didn't want to sit in her lap. I sprawled flat on my belly, weighing my desire for the biscuit and my determination to resist her closeness.

She lowered the biscuit and I tried to grab it, but she pulled it away and patted her lap again. "Come on, Spunk, up!"

Okay, she won. I jumped into her lap and grabbed the biscuit out of her hand. But I only stayed for as long as it took me to eat it. Then I scrambled out of her arms and jumped down.

In the evening, when Peter came home with Dodger, I noticed a difference in her. She strutted around the apartment with a pleased smile on her face. She followed Peter's every step. How do you like that? Now she had attached herself to my Peter!

When Daphne filled our bowls, I watched Dodger eat the huge mound of meat. Elegant. Everything she did was elegant. The way she ate, the way she lifted her head between bites to look at Daphne with appreciation, the way she lowered herself to the floor, even the way she licked her forelegs to clean them after the meal. The only thing I ever licked clean was my whiskers to get at the tasty tidbits that clung to them.

When I finished my meal, I went over to Dodger's bowl to inspect it. There was a chunk of meat in the bottom! I scooped it into my mouth. Hah! She had missed that. I looked at Dodger to see if she had noticed. She was smiling at me with utter sweetness! I was confused. Had she left that chunk of meat for me on purpose? I stared back at her for a long, thoughtful moment. Maybe she wasn't so bad after all.

9

The day of our move arrived. Peter and Daphne had finished filling up the cartons and barrels set out in the middle of the living room. For days, Daphne had been wrapping dishes and pictures, vases and lamps in newspapers and stuffing them into the barrels. Each day the apartment grew more forlorn-looking as these familiar objects were stripped away from walls and nooks and corners.

In the evenings, when Dodger came home, she inspected the emptied rooms suspiciously, whining at the vacant corners. Like me, she sensed a change coming. But she didn't have my sense of adventure.

When two muscular men came bustling into the apartment and began lifting furniture off the floor, Peter signaled for me and Dodger to follow him downstairs. He deposited us in the car.

Pointing his finger, he said, "Stay," and added, "it won't be long."

We watched the door of the apartment building. Dodger whined nervously, while I gritted my teeth. She was moving restlessly back and forth across the seat, and I hoped she wouldn't step on me.

Yah! The door opened and there were the two men. Out came our couch onto the street. Next Peter's armchair. The sight of the cozy chair sitting on the pavement made my stomach queasy. I was relieved when the men put the chair and the couch into a big truck parked in front of our car.

One by one the other pieces of our furniture were fed into the truck. Then came the barrels and cartons. They were carefully closed and sealed, their contents well buried.

Next came Mrs. Baxter. Her head was loosely covered with flowery material, which only partly hid the rows of curlers underneath. She clutched her skirt and minced toward the car, squinting with curiosity.

I smiled through the window at her, but Dodger leaped in front of me and snarled at the strange face peering through the glass. Mrs. Baxter's jaw dropped, doubling her chin. A look of horror froze her eyes. I thought she would never move, but I was wrong. Her hands suddenly flew to the sides of her head and she ran back into the building as fast as a bird flapping its wings. She didn't come out again.

At last Peter and Daphne appeared and, after a few words with the men, got into the car with us. We were on our way.

Dodger was still tense, but at least she kept to her side of the seat. Her nose was pressed against the window. I had an open window to look out of, and tried to see as much as I could as we swept along.

Soon we were turning off the highway and approaching a strangely familiar area. I sniffed the air and pricked up my ears in surprise. I knew this place. This was where I had found Peter. Yes, there were the houses Peter was building, and the rows of older houses with people living in them. I stuck my head out of the window and wagged my tail at the place I knew so well.

The car turned onto a dirt road and climbed uphill. I sniffed the trees and fields of grass we were passing, and my heart beat faster with excitement. The road curved and now I could see a large house sitting at the top of the hill. Right behind it were the looming mountains I had only seen before from a distance. The road led up to a flat stretch of land between the house and the mountains. The car came to a halt. The house was now before us in full view, and seemed enormous.

The door clicked open, and we bounded out of the car. Suddenly Dodger stopped short. The hair along her spine was standing up, and she had that wild look in her eyes again. Then I saw them too. Lying across the entrance to the house were two long-bodied coyotes. They did not stir.

"They look as if they own the place," Daphne said.

"They do," Peter replied. "They live off the land and use this house for shade and shelter. It's been empty for a long time."

The eyes of the coyotes were watching us with an infuriating indifference, slanted as though half-asleep.

"Maybe I should offer them some food. They looked half-starved," Daphne said to Peter.

"Don't. You'll never get rid of them that way."

Daphne took a few steps toward them. She bent forward and put out her hands.

"Come," she called.

One of the coyotes got up and slunk along the side of the house. The other one followed. Both had their tails between their legs.

Daphne straightened up.

"My, they're ugly!" she said.

They were. Their slippery movements made them repulsive to me.

Dodger was drooling heavily out of the corners of her mouth. Her hind legs were wide apart and her nostrils stretched. I placed my hind legs far apart too, and stood just a few paces behind her, waiting.

The snarls began. They came from deep inside Dodger's throat. Now her fangs were exposed and a snarl drew her nose far back into her face.

Now I knew what to do. I barked loudly, tossing my head about for emphasis.

Peter had Dodger by the collar and was holding on tightly. She roared at the coyotes, and the muscles of her neck bulged out of her smooth coat.

"Peter," Daphne said, "don't let Dodger go. I'm afraid of these animals."

But there was no holding Dodger back. With a powerful lunge, she freed herself from Peter's grasp, and seemed to fly through the air toward the coyotes. Soundlessly they sped away.

I ran after Dodger. Her graceful, smooth body leaped far ahead of me. A few feet from a huge boulder, Dodger stopped short. The coyotes had darted behind it and for the moment were hidden from sight. Every muscle of Dodger's body was taut. I stood beside her, waiting for the next move.

We had a glimpse of a darting head, then a tail protruding from the jutting rock. Still we held our ground. It was clear they had the advantage over us. They could rush down the slope at us much more easily than we could rush up to them. We waited.

Then Dodger began to move. Not a sound of rustling could be heard. I watched her go, instinctively knowing I could not move like that. She angled off to one side, making a wide semi-circle until she was behind and above the rock. Then she lunged down on the coyotes. I saw them dart away in different directions, yelping and pulling their tails in behind them.

When we could no longer see them, Dodger snorted her satisfaction to me. I looked up at her with undisguised admiration.

A brief smile lit her face, then with a toss of her head she motioned for me to follow. We headed back to the house. It was all ours now.

10

I was free! Truly and really free. No leash around my neck. Nobody making me do this or that.

First we ran through the rooms in the big house, sniffing everywhere, upstairs and downstairs. Each room had wide windows overlooking skies and trees and space. One enormous room had glass doors that swung out onto a circular terrace. A stone wall about three times my height surrounded the terrace. It had a wide ledge. I jumped up and could see the fields of tall grass stretching out to Peter's houses in the distance.

Dodger's head reached above the wall, so she didn't have to climb up to see the view.

Her eyes narrowed with pleasure at the vast territory that was ours. I couldn't wait to explore it and nudged Dodger's head with my nose. I jumped down and trotted across the terrace toward the back of the house. When I looked around, she wasn't following me. She was going back inside the house. I couldn't understand it. Why would she want to stay inside when there was so much to be explored outside?

I ran down the dirt road at the side of the house, through the fields toward Peter's houses, then up the road again past our house and high into the mountains in-back. With a dizzy thrill I looked down on the house. I saw the men carrying box-sized cartons on their shrunken shoulders. I was bigger than they were. And I could go anywhere I wanted.

There were thousands of twigs and leaves to sniff, each bearing the scents of unknown and unseen creatures who had been there before me. I moved through tangled bushes, and some of the creatures came out of their hiding places to poke their heads out at me. A wide-eyed rabbit blinked its eyes, then bobbled away. A rattling noise caught my attention and I glimpsed the tail end of a snake slithering away. The sound warned me of danger, and I did not pursue it. I began to sense the privacy each creature craved. Although they all fascinated me, I quickly learned not to get too close to them. Hours passed. It was an endless world of intriguing discovery.

My nostrils twitched. There was something foreign in the air. Smoke! Coming from the house. I could see the dark vapors rising above the roof. A feeling of panic gripped me, and I ran toward the house as fast as I could.

Dodger was waiting for me at the bottom of the mountain slope. When I reached her, she whined nervously and hovered over me. I stood perfectly still, not knowing what to expect. But she simply sniffed me up and down, to make sure I was unharmed. When she was satisfied that I was all right, we ran around the house to the source of the smoke. We found it was only rising from a small grill on the terrace. Peter was standing there, a platter of raw hamburger rounds balanced in his hand.

We flanked his sides and watched his every move. This was to be our first barbecue treat. Peter put the meat on the grill, and instantly it sizzled, giving off a saliva-choking fragrance.

We were wild with anticipation. When Daphne came outside with our bowls, mine had the usual layer of nuggets in it, and Dodger's had raw meat. But Peter did not fail us. With great ceremony, he broke pieces of the sizzled hamburgers into our bowls.

Delicious! Between succulent bites, I raised my eyes to Peter in reverence. He was biting into a round of meat set inside a puffy bun. Oh, it looked good. I finished eating and sat down beside him to watch him chew. Before Daphne had a chance to tell me not to pester, Peter threw me a piece of his bun. It was delightful. Sure enough, Daphne said: "Don't give her bread. It's not good for her teeth, Peter."

Dodger never had to be scolded. There she was now, sitting elegantly, a polite distance away from the table, keeping her head slightly turned to one side to avoid staring at them while they ate. How was it possible to have such good manners?

Later, when the dishes were cleared away, Daphne brought out steaming coffee for herself and Peter, and biscuits for me and Dodger. Dodger's was much bigger than mine.

Enviously, I watched the way she propped

the huge biscuit between her paws, then chopped it down with delicate side bites. I tried to prop mine up too, but the biscuit kept disappearing in the thick strands of hair around my paws. I kept trying, but finally had to nibble at it from the ground. I was only halfway through when Dodger finished eating. I got up quickly to see if she had left any crumbs. Yes, she had. While I licked them up, Dodger stretched out sideways and watched me with a little smile on her face.

When I finished the crumbs, and my own biscuit as well, I sprawled down beside Dodger. The cool stones felt pleasant against my body. Daphne and Peter sat nearby sipping their coffee and talking quietly.

"It was a good idea to rent this house from the company until I finish the project," Peter was saying.

"Yes," Daphne agreed. "Now you can keep an eye on the work going on by just sitting out here on the terrace."

"Well I may have to go down the road and mingle with the workmen now and then," Peter laughed. "A construction manager's life is not an easy one."

"When will the houses you're building in

the fields near us be ready for people to move into?" Daphne asked.

"It won't be long. You'll be having neighbors within a few months. The whole project will be completed inside a year."

"And then we'll have to leave," Daphne sighed. "What's the company planning to do with this big house?"

"They're going to make a nursing home out of it," Peter said. "Meantime you can enjoy being a pioneer woman."

"Where I come from nobody ever finds coyotes on their doorstep. I'm used to having people nearby."

Peter grew thoughtful. "Maybe we should have another watchdog around here."

Daphne gazed over the stone ledge, and pointed toward the far side of the fields. "I wonder if anyone is living in that broken-down shack over there."

"That used to be the caretaker's cottage for this place. These fields were once a vineyard."

I had seen that cottage from the mountain slope. It was curious-looking, sitting there all alone in a field of grass. It seemed to be falling apart.

While Peter and Daphne talked, I began

reliving the wonders of the day. I had roamed the mountain with no leash around my neck. I had been free. Suddenly I realised that instead of running away, as I had so often planned, I was lying here next to big Dodger, with no desire to go anywhere.

A wary uneasiness came over me. I never wanted to lose my freedom again. Tomorrow I would run off as far as I wanted to go, do whatever I wanted to do, see whatever I wanted to see. I'd start with that curious little cottage.

These promises of adventure soothed my ruffled feelings and I began to doze.

Maybe, I thought, a moment before falling asleep, I would just come home for dinner.

During the night I was jarred awake again and again by the howling of coyotes and shrieking rabbits. But Dodger's comforting closeness kept lulling me back to sleep, until another sound awakened me: the roar of a car getting louder and louder. It was coming up the dirt road toward our house.

A light flashed on in the hall, and I saw Peter coming downstairs with a flashlight in his hand. Daphne was behind him, pulling a robe over her nightgown.

Dodger ran to Peter's side, whining nervously. Together they went outside through the kitchen door. I jumped onto the kitchen windowsill, using the chair beneath as a step. Daphne was crouched behind the half-windowed door, peering out through the parted curtains.

The car swerved around to the back of the house and came to a screeching halt. The car door opened and a light inside greased the faces of two men sitting on the front seat. They were smiling. Only their smiles had a twisted look, and didn't reach their eyes.

Peter had a firm hold on Dodger's collar. "You're on private property," he said sternly.

The man close to the open door swung his legs out and leaned toward Peter. "We like private property," he answered. Both men were laughing now, a shrill sound that made my spine hairs rise. I scratched at the screen, whimpering, trying to warn Peter.

Dodger was straining forward with all her might, her tail twitching fast. The next moment, she had bolted out of Peter's grasp and was springing at the man. He fell back on the seat. Roaring with fury, Dodger leaped inside the car. The men thrashed about wildly, screaming in terror.

Peter lunged after Dodger, grabbed her collar, and pulled her out of the car. He slammed the door shut. A moment later the engine roared and the car screeched away, stuttering to gain speed.

Peter and Dodger stood together watching the car until it disappeared. Then they came back to the house. I was at the door beside Daphne when she opened it and fell into Peter's arms, trembling and sobbing. Peter stroked her head.

"We won't see those jokers back again," he said.

Daphne knelt down and threw her arms around Dodger. Tears were running down her cheeks. Dodger licked them away.

Peter patted Dodger's shoulder. "You did a fine job," he said. There was deep respect in his voice, and Dodger beamed, quivering with pride.

I went back to bed.

11

I ran through the fields until I reached the small cottage. There was a covered garbage can at the back door, which I knew would contain many treasures. I began to sniff around it.

Suddenly the door swung open and an old, bent woman appeared in the doorway, squinting down at me.

"What are you doing there?" she grumbled. I wagged my tail at her.

"Hungry, eh?" she said. I brushed up against her leg, then sat myself down on her foot and looked up into her face.

"Wait here a minute," she said and went inside the cottage. In a few moments she came out with a cookie in her hand. Peter and Daphne ate cookies, but they never gave me any. Daphne said it was bad for my teeth. The old woman tossed the cookie to me and I gobbled it down. It was sweet, so delicious. I licked my lips and nudged the woman's leg with my head.

"Come inside," she said. "And I'll give you another cookie."

I followed her into the cottage.

Once inside, she shut the door quickly.

"There now," she said. "You can stay with me and be my little doggie. You'll get all the cookies you want."

My heart beat faster. The odors inside the room were stale and uninviting. My hair began to prickle my skin. I pressed the side of my body against the door and barked.

"Don't you want your cookie?" the woman asked in a high-pitched voice. She reached for a cardboard box on the table and made a big fuss about taking one out. Then she dangled it over my head, moving her hand back and forth enticingly.

I leaped up to get the cookie and bit her hand instead. She screamed and the cookie went flying into the air. It landed in bits on the floor. In a fury, she opened the door, her eyes wide with anger. Out I ran.

"You bad dog!" she screamed after me.

I ran through the fields back to our house. The path was thick with jagged bushes and I could feel little needle points biting into my skin, but I kept running. In a little while I reached the terrace.

They were both there—Daphne in the wicker armchair, reading a book, Dodger lying peacefully at her feet.

I walked over to Daphne and sat down beside her chair. She continued reading, but absent-mindedly began stroking my head and back.

"Ouch!" she cried and pulled her hand away. "What on earth have you gotten into?"

She bent down and examined me.

"You're full of stickers!" she cried. "Why do you always have to bring half of California home with you?" she asked.

I looked at her sideways. Could I help it if my long hair curled around twigs and leaves and pulled them from their branches?

The job of picking the needle-sharp burrs out of my tangled hair was taking her a long time. When she was through with the top part of me, I lay down on my back, with my paws in the air, so she could do my stomach as well.

"Oh, Spunky!" she sighed when she saw how much more there was still left to be picked out.

My thoughts drifted back to the little cottage, where the cookie was left splattered on the floor. I knew I would never go back there again.

That night, after dinner, I made my first attack. I had learned a lot from Dodger.

I was sprawled on my belly, trying to enjoy the after-taste of my meal. But every few minutes the spiteful fly whizzed by over my head, jarring me out of my comfortable spot.

Dodger was nearby, blinking her eyes sleepily, and from time to time licking bits of crumbs from her smooth, shiny coat. Daphne and Peter were sipping coffee and talking quietly at their little table on the terrace.

I waited for the right moment. It was coming toward me again. I sat up and nonchalantly scratched my ear—perfectly relaxed, as if nothing unusual was about to happen. But I watched it out of the corner of my eye. I kept my head slightly tilted to get a clear view while scratching away, pretending I was totally absorbed by my ear.

There it was. I leaped into the air and struck. Down it came. I sniffed the ground until I found it, lying on its back, kicking its feet, stunned but alive. I bared my teeth and growled. It just lay there, trembling and helpless. Then I struck again, first one paw, then the other. I snarled ferociously with each heavy blow.

Now I would finish it off. With a quick twist of my head, I picked it off the ground. But it got caught in my whiskers. I shook my head fitfully until it landed on the ground again. Then, with deadly accuracy, I struck with my paw, finishing its life completely.

Dodger got up to inspect my work. When she saw the dead fly, she snorted her satisfaction to me. I was well pleased.

Daphne and Peter were also curious to see what I had done. They leaned over us, squinting down at the ground. When they saw the dead fly, they burst into laughter.

"Spunky, you're a tiger," Daphne declared merrily, and ruffled my coat.

"Good work, Spunk," Peter said, chuckling to himself.

What was so funny? They didn't laugh when Dodger made her attacks.

* * *

The next evening I spotted a cat chasing through our fields. Now I would really show them. The cat had no right to be on our territory, and the way it scurried in front of me stirred up my taste for battle.

It sure could run fast. But it was no match for me. We reached the big lemon tree at the side of our house and the cat scampered up the trunk. Now I had it.

Its eyes glared down at me from the branch above. The hairs on its body were standing straight up like needles.

I circled the tree, stamping my paws and barking. I stood under the branch and snarled my anger. But the cat would not budge. I raised myself on my hind legs and scratched the bark with my front paws.

Suddenly the cat lunged. I felt its sharp claws pierce my nose and mouth. My cries of pain brought Dodger running from the house. The cat darted away, and Dodger followed. But she soon returned with a defeated drag to her walk. The cat was gone.

When we went inside the house, Daphne took one look at me and gasped. Quickly she brought out the medicine kit and dabbed a cotton pad coated with ointment over my wounds. I tried to squirm away from her.

Dodger moaned in sympathy, but Daphne kept scolding.

"Fighting with cats! You ought to know better than that. Don't you ever go near a cat again. Remember — NO MORE CATS.

She was right. No more cats for me. For once I agreed with her.

But a few days later, Dodger and I were out early, running in the fields. Everything was waking up and sunlight was just beginning to sparkle through the trees.

Suddenly Dodger stopped short, legs frozen wide apart, head thrust straight forward, tail trembling. I followed her gaze and saw it too — the cat. The memory of those sharp claws came back to me, and I had no taste to pursue it. But Dodger began to move stealthily through the bushes. Reluctantly, I followed.

Now it saw us, and quickly scampered up the nearest tree. There was a hollow high up in the trunk, and the cat hid inside. She was well protected from Dodger's long reach.

I backed away from the tree and made whimpering, pleading sounds in my throat, pressing against Dodger. She paid no attention to me. Her spine hairs were stiff now. Frustration was making the saliva drool down the corners of her mouth.

There was no budging her. And the cat was safe. With each passing moment, Dodger grew more and more frantic, snarling and barking up at the quiet cat.

Time passed. The sun was high above the mountains now. Dodger's bark was hoarse. I knew she would stay there forever if she had to.

I felt helpless. I had to get her away from that tree. Her powerful muscles rippled as she stalked around it. Her thick snarls blocked out any sounds I made. I needed someone to help me. Someone who could handle Dodger. Peter was at work. He could be anywhere between his trailer and all those houses being built. He would be hard to find. There was only Daphne. It would have to be Daphne.

I ran all the way back to the house, taking a shortcut through the fields. Daphne was outside on the terrace, polishing the windows. She didn't notice me. I stood behind her, panting heavily, waiting.

At last she turned her head and saw me. I wagged my tail nervously, my mouth half open and dry.

"Spunky, what's the matter?" she asked.

I backed up a few paces and kept looking at her, my tongue dangling loosely.

84

"What is it?" she demanded.

I moved sideways, keeping my eyes on her, and tilted my head in the direction of the fields. Her face was puckered up and perplexed, but she moved toward me slowly, the polishing cloth still in her hand.

I edged backward, my tail between my legs, heading toward the fields. Daphne followed me more quickly. I waved my tail and started to trot, turning my head to see if she was still behind me. She was.

I ran to the dirt road leading to the fields. Then took the shortcut through the thick bushes to reach Dodger faster.

"Spunky," Daphne called out. "I can't run through those bushes."

I stopped short and doubled back to her. I ran ahead of her along the curving road until it thinned out and we could cut across the fields easily.

When we reached the tree, Dodger was frightening to see. Her snarls had become moans and her whole body was trembling.

Daphne went up to her.

"What've you got there, Dodger?" she asked. Dodger stared up at the hollow.

"A cat!" Daphne exclaimed. Dodger whined loudly, and pressed up against her.

Daphne watched Dodger thoughtfully for

a moment, then with a firm, quick grasp, she took hold of Dodger's collar.

"Home," she ordered.

Dodger whimpered and tugged at her collar, but Daphne held firm.

"Come on. Back to the house."

Still whimpering, but obedient to Daphne's command, Dodger trotted beside her back along the dirt road.

I followed behind them. Glancing back at the tree, I saw the cat leap out of the hollow and dart away through the fields. What a relief to see it go.

Suddenly I realized I had done something I had never thought possible. I had asked Daphne for help, and she had understood what I wanted.

A feeling of happiness seemed to lift me off the ground as I trotted behind them. I did not take the shortcut through the fields.

Dodger and I could not understand Daphne at times. All the wonderful things we enjoyed, like rattlesnakes, skunks, or wild mice that visited our house once in a while, made her shiver, gasp, or scream.

Once I found a dead rattlesnake lying on the road to our house. But I knew better than to bring it home. Daphne would only scream.

But Dodger had the worst time of it. Especially with the birds. Every now and then a bird would fly straight into the glass doors overlooking the terrace. It would fall to the ground stunned. Dodger loved when this happened. It was almost impossible to catch a bird in flight. Her hunting instincts were well satisfied when she could grab a falling bird between her teeth. As long as Daphne wasn't around.

Late one afternoon, Daphne was out on the terrace with us. A bird flew into the window and fell to the ground. Dodger lunged forward and made the grab.

"No! No!" Daphne screamed.

Dodger looked up, bewildered, but obediently dropped the bird from her mouth. Her self-control truly amazed me.

Daphne picked up the still bird, and brought it into the house. We followed her. Inside the kitchen, she filled an eyedropper with water and squeezed a few drops into the bird's beak.

Then she made a bed for it of soft cotton stuffed into a shoe box. She put it on a high shelf in the kitchen and waited.

It wasn't long before the bird started to flap its wings. Daphne took the box outside, lifted out the bird, and put it on one of the branches of the lemon tree. After watching it for a time, she went back into the house.

Dodger and I waited to see if the bird would fly away. It sat still for a long while. Then it started to wobble a bit. It finally tumbled off the branch down to the ground. Dodger made the grab.

She looked around carefully, the bird between her teeth, to make sure Daphne was still inside. Then she carried the bird to the far side of the house and dug a hole in the ground with her paws. When it was deep enough, she dropped the dead bird into the hole and scratched loose dirt over it.

Daphne came outside again to inspect the tree branch, and Dodger ran up to her with a big smile on her face.

"Where's the bird?" Daphne asked pleasantly.

Dodger was thoroughly fooled.

She ran to the side of the house and dug up the bird, then proudly trotted back to Daphne with the dead bird between her teeth.

Daphne screamed.

I thought Dodger would never learn.

12

Dodger and I were waiting for Peter. There was a clear, beautiful sunset, like many others we had watched together in the past few months. We had no inkling that when Peter arrived we would be in for a surprise.

We spotted his car from the stone ledge and ran down the road to meet him, running and leaping alongside the car until it came to a stop.

But when Peter got out, there were no head-rubbings for us. In his arms was a small, trembling black dog. We barked wildly, feet wide apart in attack position.

Peter lowered the shivering dog to the ground and straightened up.

"Say hello to Happy," he said calmly.

Our barking faltered at the tone of his voice. But we kept our stance.

Daphne came running out of the house. She looked at the trembling dog and began to laugh. "Don't tell me this is your idea of another watchdog!"

"No," replied Peter. "This one *needs* watching. One of my workmen had to give him up. So I brought him home."

Daphne's eyes widened as she looked at the three of us. Then she shook her head as if to clear her mind.

"Well, let's see how they take to one another. Bring him around to the terrace. Come on, Dodger, Spunky."

Peter lifted Happy off the ground and carried him in his arms. We followed close behind. When we reached the terrace, Peter set Happy down on the stone floor and then joined Daphne at the table.

In a second, Happy had darted under the wicker couch against the side wall. We roared our anger into the narrow space that hid him. A shiny nose protruded for just a moment, then quickly withdrew.

By flattening my body to the ground, I was able to look underneath the couch. There he was, pressed against the wall, shivering. I stared at him, and the eyes blinked back at me, wet with suffering.

I backed away from the couch, whining up at Dodger to do the same. We had to give him a chance to come out. Dodger looked at me in surprise. It had never occurred to her to leave her prey for even a moment, but this was a dog Peter had brought home. We had to remember that. Dodger understood, and backed away with slow, deliberate steps, her tail twitching with tension.

We waited, without barking, staring at the space under the couch. Would Happy have the guts to come out? Quiet, no movement. Then the small black head poked out. There was a patch of white on his forehead, just between his eyes. He stared at us cautiously. We kept our position.

Soon the rest of him came out. He sat himself up rigidly in front of the couch, pressing his back against it for support. The small, heart-shaped face strained forward. The eyes stared straight ahead. He was waiting for our decision.

Dodger nodded to me. She would let me handle this.

My approach was unhurried, my tail waving with authority behind me. I stood over Happy, sniffing expertly.

He was just a pup. About half my size. Kind of funny-looking too. He had a muscular, cigar-shaped body, with short, thick legs and smooth hair. He was completely black, except for that triangular patch of white between his eyes. He was as shiny and clean-smelling as fresh laundry. The eyes looked past me while I made my examination. Good control.

I had to test it. Very casually, I strolled away from him. Then with a sudden movement I rushed right at him. Not a muscle moved, only the eyes, squinting with the effort of keeping still.

I moved away, planning my next move. A double somersault. I landed at his feet, panting, and looked up into his eyes. They darted down at me, pleading for kindness, then stared straight ahead again. Not another muscle twitched. I glanced at Dodger. A hint of a smile crossed her face. She was impressed, but her tail was still twitching nervously.

I got up and sniffed the wet tilted nose. Only a blink of the eyes. What admirable control, and here I was, towering over him. Oh, I liked him. What fun we could have together. I could show him all the fascinating places I had discovered in the mountains. I could teach him so many things: how to chase rabbits and how to get away from hissing snakes. I wondered how fast Happy could run with those short legs.

But now it was up to Dodger. Would she let him stay? Would she do it for me? I whined up at her, searching her face anxiously.

Her shoulders were stiff with tension, her head lowered by the burden of making her decision.

I returned to Happy, who was sitting still, bravely waiting. I sniffed his nose. His eyes were begging now. Oh, how I wanted him to stay. I whined softly. Please, could Happy stay? Dodger looked at me with a tenderness that reached deep inside me. Then slowly and elegantly she lowered herself to the ground. Happy could stay!

Daphne got up and quickly patted all of us.

"Looks like three for dinner tonight," she said to Peter.

Was this the same dog who had begged for mercy a few days ago? The dog who had shown so much control? It couldn't be.

From the top of the stone ledge, I was watching him being put through his paces. Daphne was teaching him to "Sit" and "Stay" and all that boring stuff. But he couldn't sit still for more than half a second. All he wanted to do was run around and play.

And could he run. I had never seen anything so fast in all my life. Tumbling with him absolutely dumbfounded me. Just when I thought I was landing on top of him, he was right behind me with that silly grin on his face, wagging that long, skinny black tail of his.

You'd think I would have his company in the mountains? No such thing. All he wanted to do was run through the fields, visit Peter and the new people living in the houses already finished. Once I heard Daphne talking on the phone with one of them.

"Yes, I have a little black dog, Happy. . . .

What's he doing over there? . . . Visiting . . . He did what? Well, just tell him to go home."

Then back he'd come. Full of kisses for everyone. I never saw such a kissing dog. That's all he ever seemed to do when he stayed still long enough.

Daphne's voice broke into my thoughts: "Spunk, come down and show Happy how to stay."

What did she want from me? I jumped down and ambled over to her. Happy watched us with that silly grin.

"Stay," she commanded. Where was my biscuit? I sniffed around her to see if she had one. Yes, in her pocket. She better have it ready for me or I wouldn't perform. I walked around until she took it out of her pocket.

"Now sit," she said sharply. I sat.

"Stay!" she said, and walked across the terrace. When she came back, she gave me the one small biscuit. It was something, anyway.

"Okay, Happy. Now it's your turn."

I jumped back on top of the ledge and watched. Dodger was lying in the shade, waiting for Daphne to get through with Happy's training for the day. Then we would take over and teach him the really important things, like barking at the milkman and the mailman. In the past week we had devoted a lot of our time to him.

He was still getting milk and raw egg in his nuggets. I must admit, that first night I had a twinge of envy when I saw what he had in his bowl. It made me miss my early puppy days. Milk and raw egg is so delicious.

I had waited patiently for Happy to finish his first meal with us, knowing how much it meant to him. When he was done, I inspected his bowl for left-overs. Not a thing. Clean as can be. At least Dodger never failed me. She always left a chunk of meat in her bowl for me.

When Daphne brought out our after-dinner biscuits that night, I knew Happy would love them. I hid mine under my paw and waited until he and Dodger had both finished eating. Then I sprawled on my belly and waved my tail behind me to attract Happy's attention. Now I would have my fun. I lifted my paw off the ground. There it was, my biscuit — whole and uneaten. Happy's eyes widened when he saw it. Just as I expected.

Happy couldn't tear his eyes away. He

wanted it. Just as I figured. I put my paw down beside the biscuit and turned my head ever so slightly. He made a lunge for it. Hah! I had my paw back over it before he knew what was happening. Now he lost all pretence at good behavior. He crouched on the ground face to face with me, waiting for his next chance.

I held the biscuit between my teeth, halfway protruding out of my mouth so he could see it clearly. Then I sat up and with a toss of my head sailed it high into the air. Happy leaped up, but the biscuit fell to the ground right beside me, and I had my paw over it before he could see where it went.

When I lifted my paw, he lunged and I growled at him. Immediately he corrected himself, sitting up erectly, his eyes wincing with the effort of control.

Then I carefully propped the biscuit up between my paws, just the way Dodger did, and bit the top part off — so delicious, as Happy knew. Between bites, I licked my whiskers in appreciation. Happy winced. Dodger was smiling at us. She was enjoying my game.

My after-dinner biscuit had never been more satisfying.

13

The high-pitched yapping was coming from the fields. I ran down the slope, following the urgent sound. Was Happy in trouble?

When I came close, I saw what it was. A man on horseback was galloping across our fields. Happy was running alongside the horse's front legs, never losing pace for an instant and yapping up at the rider. The man was shouting at Happy to get away.

I decided to help out. I took up a position at the horse's hind legs, running apace and barking. The horse kicked out at me several times, but missed. This only increased the fun. The rider yelled down at me; a fine spray of spittle accompanied his shouting.

Suddenly the horse reared up on its hind legs, and the man slid off its back to the ground. Happy and I ran over to him. We sniffed him up and down. His dazed face was wet with sweat, and steam seemed to be oozing out of him.

That silly Happy began kissing the man's face. With a burst of energy, the man made a grab for Happy, but his hand only grasped a bunch of weeds. Happy was already behind him. This seemed to give the man a fresh surge of energy. He raised himself off the ground and came stumbling after us.

Happy darted between his legs, underneath his outstretched arms, and right through his outstretched hands. At last the exhausted man simply dropped his arms to his sides and shuffled over to his horse. With his last bit of strength he lifted himself into the saddle, wiggled the reins, and eased the horse along without once glancing back at us. We let him go. It was almost dinnertime anyway.

The houses were coming closer. A new row of wooden skeletons was going up in our fields. During the day the sound of hammering could be heard throughout our house. When the sun started to go down, the workmen stopped and left the skeletons standing there, empty and strangely quiet.

The three of us ran together through the fields to inspect the new skeletons. We ran in and out of the wooden frames, one by one, sniffing everything we found. In one of them we found skeleton stairs that led up to a low-ceilinged room. We climbed the rough, unfinished planks one by one. Nothing upstairs but wood shavings and sawdust, with nails strewn around, just like everywhere else. We ran down again.

When we reached the bottom, we realized Happy was not with us. We looked around, then up the stairs. There he was at the very top, looking down at us with eyes blinking back fear. He was afraid to come down. That small head made the wide spaces between each stair seem even wider. It was easy to see he could fall between the spaces if he missed a landing.

It was beginning to grow dark and menacing shadows loomed everywhere. We were anxious to leave.

Dodger and I ran up the stairs. Happy welcomed us eagerly and pranced around our legs. To show him there was nothing to it, we ran down the stairs again. When we looked back, Happy's little black head, with the white patch between the eyes, was still stiffly poised at the top step.

No matter how much Dodger whimpered up at him, and no matter how invitingly we pranced about below, he would not come down.

What could we do? For a long time we circled around at the foot of the stairs. But it was so dark now, only the white patch could be seen above. Finally Dodger lowered her head in resignation. We had to go home. With a nod of her head, she motioned for me to follow. We had to leave Happy behind.

When we reached the house, Daphne was waiting for us. Dodger and I moved slowly toward her, guilt making us drag our tails between our legs. Dodger kept ducking her head as if to avoid a blow.

"Where's Happy?" Daphne asked. It was like the crack of a whip. Dodger backed away as if struck.

"Where's Happy?" Daphne repeated. Her voice seemed to shriek in our ears.

I tossed my head in the direction of the houses. Daphne moved toward me.

"Come on, show me."

We had no choice. We had to show her how we had left Happy behind.

Our tails hung low as we guiltily led her through the fields.

As we got closer to the skeleton house, we could hear Happy's yapping. A pitiful, fearful sound.

We led Daphne to the foot of the stairs and looked up. In the darkness, all we could see was the wet shine of his eyes and the white patch.

Daphne cautiously climbed the stairs and took Happy into her arms. She brought him down carefully, step by step. He was covering her face with kisses.

As soon as he was placed on the ground, he pranced around us with that silly grin on his face. For some reason he was proud of himself.

Daphne patted his head, which only added to his joy. Then she turned to us.

"Thank you, Dodger, Spunk, for bringing me to Happy."

The gentle tone of her voice seeped through us and took the guilt away. All of a sudden we too felt proud. All the way home, Dodger and I trotted close to Daphne. Crazy Happy ran far ahead of us, then doubled back to rejoin us, again and again.

14

Peter had made a crackling fire in the living room, and we were all huddled around the fire place. The night was damp and chilly. Rainy days had come again.

"I think I've finally found another good watchdog for us," Peter said. "There's a woman not far from here who breeds Weimaraners, like Dodger. I called her today, and she has a fine male dog for us to look at."

"I wonder if Dodger would allow a strange male dog in the house."

"Happy's a male."

"Yes, but he's just a pup, so small and harmless."

"Well, I think we should give it a try."

"Who knows," said Daphne. "If Dodger likes him, maybe we'll have some little Weimaraners running around."

"Good. Then it's settled. We'll go and see the woman on Sunday. Maybe we can kill two birds with one stone!"

"Don't talk about killing birds in front of Dodger," Daphne said in a low whisper.

Peter smiled. "You think they understand everything we say, don't you?"

"I have good reason to believe they do." Daphne looked at me when she said that.

On Sunday we drove to a house hidden by thick foliage and surrounded by huge trees. When we turned into the driveway we could see large, squared-off, wire-mesh enclosures behind the house. Each held one or two dogs who looked like Dodger. They all began running around and barking as we drove up.

Happy and I were told to stay inside the car. Only Dodger was taken out. Daphne attached a leash to her collar and held her firmly against her side.

A sturdy, quick-moving woman came out of the house. She shushed the dogs, then turned to Peter and Daphne.

"How do you do," Daphne said. They exchanged handshakes and smiles, then Daphne pointed to Happy and me peering out of the car window.

"That's the rest of our family," she said.

The woman's eyes flickered over us and dismissed us the next instant. She turned her full attention to Dodger. Out of her pocket came a tape measure. With nimble fingers she stretched the tape across Dodger's back, up along her flank, then across her chest. Wrists and fingers sped along as she bent her head in deep concentration. Dodger's tail was twitching, but I could see she was impressed by this woman.

"Good stance," the woman declared. "Although the hip spread is a little narrow. A little too small-boned for a purebred Weimaraner."

She lifted Dodger's upper lip with her thumb.

"Good teeth. Do you have papers on her?"

"No, we don't." There was some hesitation in Daphne's voice.

"All my Weimaraners are top breed. I have the entire history of each and every one of them. Wait here a moment. I'll bring out the book on Eric."

While they waited, Dodger pressed close to Daphne's side, shifting her legs uneasily.

The woman came out with a huge book, and they all sat down together on a bench underneath a tree near the car.

The woman held the book in her lap and turned the pages.

"This is Eric's mother." The woman pointed to a picture. "His full name is Eric von Stromberger, The Third."

Peter was scratching his head, and a tiny smile played at the corners of his mouth.

The woman turned the pages and made comments about Eric's father, brothers, sisters, ancestors, and the medals he had won throughout the country, mostly for good behavior.

Finally she put the book aside and walked to one of the wire fences and clapped her hands.

"Eric," she called. "Come."

Even from this distance we could see that Eric was something special. He was bigger than Dodger and very handsome. He leaped through the grass with rippling grace, smiling pleasantly.

The woman opened a little gate and led Eric over to where Dodger stood, spine hairs stiffly raised. Dodger's tail began to twitch nervously, and that wild look had come back into her eyes.

Eric kept smiling, and gingerly tried to nuzzle Dodger's head. She backed away fitfully, grunting her indignation. Eric shifted his stance. Playfully, he romped to one side and further away from Dodger. The hairs along Dodger's spine began to soften.

"Let's put them inside the pen and see what happens," the woman said.

Daphne led Dodger through the gate. Eric followed and the gate was closed behind them.

Eric showed off his fine stride, running gracefully around the pen. Dodger stood very still, watching his every move. From time to time Eric ran close to Dodger but always passed by without touching her. Finally, he stopped in front of her and thrust his face forward. Their noses touched. Dodger's tail wagged, and Eric leaped about happily.

"She likes him," the woman declared.

"In that case," said Daphne, "we'll take him home with us."

Eric was willingly led into the car and sat in front between Happy and Peter. Daphne, Dodger, and I sat in the back. Eric kept his head turned around to us all the way home, but he hardly glanced at me. His eyes were focused on Dodger. But Dodger had her head out the window and was snapping at cars that passed by.

Eric made his first mistake the moment we arrived home. Without thinking, he went through the door of our house first. Dodger nipped him in the ear with a grunt, making him stagger back in shock. Then she lifted her head and went through the door ahead of him. Eric bowed meekly and trailed behind us.

Outside on the terrace, however, he quickly recovered his pride and eagerness to show off. At Daphne's command, he would sit, stay, and come with unfailing ease. On top of that, he knew how to heel. Something Daphne had never taught us.

With resentful admiration, I watched him heel. When Daphne gave the command, Eric marched beside her, up and down the terrace. When Daphne stopped walking, he sat down at her heels.

Dodger was impressed and pawed the ground, eager for her turn. Eric stood by watching good-naturedly as Daphne taught Dodger how to heel. She learned quickly and seemed to enjoy the whole thing.

I was bored.

I sat on top of the stone ledge with my head slightly turned toward the fields. But out of the corner of my eye I watched the activity on the terrace.

Now Daphne was ordering Eric and Dodger to heel together on either side of her. I must admit they did it beautifully, but dumb little Happy kept running around them until they both lost stride and nearly tripped.

Daphne didn't bother to ask me to do anything. Not that I wanted to. It was all so silly. Still, a feeling of being locked out crept over me. I lowered my chin on my paw and sulked. Why did I stay here with them?

The three of them were making me sick.

The amount of food Eric consumed was incredible. I had never seen such portions of raw meat in a bowl. He gulped it all down in rapid mouthfuls and then looked around for more. He sniffed Dodger's bowl while she was still eating, but she nipped him away quickly. He would have to learn that Dodger's leftovers were mine and mine only. Not even Happy got to lick Dodger's bowl until I was absolutely through with it.

When Dodger had eaten, I walked over to her bowl to get my bits of meat. I looked at the bowl in amazement. There was nothing left. Dodger had forgotten to leave something for me. I felt more closed out than ever.

Inside the den that night, I tried to fall asleep. It was impossible. All night long, I watched Eric trying to maneuver close to Dodger, and being snarled back each time. But Happy was allowed to lie up against her whenever he chose.

I had had enough. I decided to show the three of them how I felt.

Just before dawn, I got out of my bed, walked to the middle of the den, and wet right in the middle of the floor.

That got their attention. Three heads jerked up, eyes wide in horror. They scrambled to their feet and ran out through the screen flap one by one. Dodger first, of course.

I settled back into my bed and went to sleep, contented at last. When Daphne came into the room, her gasp woke me up. But I pretended to be asleep, and buried my head in my cushion.

"What's this?" she cried in disbelief. I raised my head, my eyes half-closed.

"Spunky! You did that." How could she tell?

"You bad dog!" She chased me out the door.

I trotted down to the field, just as Dodger, Happy, and Eric were returning to the house. They passed by with their heads lowered. Dodger glanced at me nervously for a moment, then looked away. I felt good. I could get away with anything, and I wanted them all to know it.

When I returned to the house, it was all cleaned up and Daphne had forgotten all about it. The three of them had forgotten all about it too, and all about me as well. They were once again absorbed in one another, just as before.

That night I did the same thing. Dodger moaned, and they all ran out before Daphne got up.

This time when she saw the puddle, she was angrier than the day before. She whacked my behind as I went through the screen flap. Now I really had her going.

So the next morning I did it again.

This time Daphne flew into a rage. I had never seen her so angry. When I ran outside, she ran after me and hit me so hard I squealed.

When I passed by the side of the house, Dodger grunted her disapproval at me. I didn't even look at her. I kept right on walking.

This time, I decided, I would not go back to the house. I went to the old lemon tree, and sank down into the thick grass.

I could see the house, but no one could see me. There was Dodger coming around the side of the house, making her inspection tour. Happy was right beside her. Eric strolled behind at the appropriate distance. When Happy dashed under Eric's feet, the big dog snapped impatiently. Dodger's head turned sharply and a look of disapproval was directed at Eric. He bowed his head meekly in apology. Hah! Happy was like a fly that Eric couldn't shake off. I sank lower into the ground. Life seemed unbearable.

The sun started to go down. Peter's car drove up, but still I didn't move. The three of them greeted him. I watched and listened with a lump in my throat. Soon barbecue smoke began rising up above the roof of the house. I could smell the delicious meat sizzling. Still I remained where I was.

I could hear the clinking of bowls and dishes on the terrace. I closed my eyes and wished I could close my ears and nose as well.

"Where's Spunky?" I heard Peter ask. Then Daphne called my name. Her voice came closer. She was coming around the side of the house. She was looking for me. I did not move. Suddenly she was standing right above me.

"Spunky," she exclaimed softly. She knelt down beside me. "Don't you want your dinner?" I did not look up, but kept my chin on the ground. Daphne stroked my head.

"I'm sorry I hit you, Spunk." Her hand was as gentle as a breeze. "You know I love you more than anything in the world." Her voice jelled in her throat.

Then she put her hand under my chin and raised my head. I looked into her eyes. There were tears in them. She kissed my nose. I wagged my tail and quickly got up.

We trotted back to the house together. My appetite was quite good, after all.

Eric's control was wearing thin. Happy did not leave him alone for a moment. Sometimes, if Dodger was not looking, Eric snapped at Happy in anger. But Happy was as stubborn as a fly.

One rainy Saturday afternoon, the four of us were in the den. For the first time Eric had managed to lie down close to Dodger without being snapped away. Happy was jealously hovering over them, yapping at Eric shrilly.

Eric raised his head, and with a sudden movement bit into Happy.

My ears stood straight up. I thought Happy's head was bitten off. Dodger staggered to her feet, stiff with alarm. Her hind legs wobbled until she balanced herself. Happy was shrieking in pain. Blood oozed over his eyes and mouth.

Daphne ran into the room. She looked frozen, her mouth open in horror. In another moment Peter was there. Quickly he lifted Happy into his arms and carried him out to the car. Daphne followed, and they drove away. The house became silent.

A small pool of blood darkened the floor, where Happy had stood. Dodger and I huddled close together and stared at it.

Eric whined and moved toward us. A gurgling snarl burst out of Dodger's throat, and Eric staggered back as if shoved. He retreated to a far corner of the room, whimpering.

Dodger's rage erupted in thundering snarls. She paced back and forth in front of Eric, shoulders hunched, nostrils flaring, her nose drawn back in thick, quivering folds. The room and everything in it trembled. Eric cringed and whimpered deep in his corner.

But the attack did not come. Dodger's jaws finally grew slack and her pacing stopped. She sank to the floor, shivering, and looked about the room. Her bewildered gaze rested on me for a long moment, appealing and helpless. I had to comfort her. When I sprawled down close beside her, she sighed deeply.

She did not look at Eric again. It was as if he were no longer in the room.

15

I stayed close to Dodger for the next few days. The house was quiet without Happy. Eric was gone. He had been taken back to the woman that very same night. Daphne's voice shook when she commanded him to "Heel," but he followed her out of the house with meek, light steps.

Each day Daphne went to visit Happy. We could smell fresh whiffs of Happy's scent on her clothing when she returned home. It stirred us with expectation, but all we could do was wait.

At last, one afternoon when Daphne returned, she stepped out of the car and Happy was in her arms. We went wild with joy. A large white bandage covered Happy's head, but he looked down at us with that same silly grin. We leaped about and ran in circles until Daphne lowered him to the ground. Dodger solemnly sniffed him up and down, whining at the medicine smell of the bandages. Happy stood perfectly still for the inspection, his eyes blinking out his suffering to us.

Daphne carried him inside the house and lit the fireplace in the living room. She brought Happy's bed close to the crackling flames, and he snuggled into it with sighs of contentment. We stretched out beside him on the floor, and soon a cozy warmth spread over the three of us. It was so good to have Happy back.

For a while, everything was back to normal. Happy's wound healed and left only a tiny scar above his eye. I resumed my wanderings on the mountain, and Dodger guarded all of us with renewed vigor. I had no inkling that soon everything would change. I took all the days we enjoyed for granted, even the day I learned to swim.

Peter came home early that day and declared he was taking us all to the beach. From the tone of his voice, we knew we

were in for a special treat. We were filled
with excitement. The three of us were in the
back seat. Dodger had her head out the window on Daphne's side of the car, and I leaned
out of Peter's side. Poor Happy was in the
middle, trying to stretch his neck up. He
could have looked out of the back window,
but I wasn't about to tell him that.

When we got close to the beach, the air
became laden with the tantalizing smells
of fish and seaweed. We sniffed the air
hungrily, but Peter did not stop until we
came to a parking area on top of a cliff.
Down below were jagged rocks. At the very
bottom was a strip of sand where the ocean
burst into foaming waves, then withdrew
to sparkle against the sky. The water returned again and again with a fresh burst
of foam.

Happy was first at the water's edge, leaping back and forth with the movement of
the curling waves. Dodger heeled alongside
Peter and Daphne as they walked toward
the water.

I was completely absorbed smelling the
empty shells strewn along the sand until I
heard Dodger moan. I looked up just in time
to see Peter and Daphne running into the
waves. The water was making them dis-

appear. Only their arms and heads were visible above the whirlpools of foam. I ran to join Dodger and Happy. We pawed the wet sand nervously, watching Peter and Daphne getting farther and farther away from us. The cold, bubbling water brushed against our paws, making us pull back into the warm, dry sand.

Then I heard a familiar sound: Peter's chuckle. Then Daphne's laugh rang out. I could see them splashing at one another, ducking their heads, smiles on their faces. They were having fun.

I had to go to them. The sand became soggy, and then it began to slip beneath my paws. I kept moving. The cold water was under my belly now and carrying me along. Dodger was moaning, and Happy was barking at me frantically from the water's edge. But I did not turn back. I kept moving my paws and miraculously I was coming closer to them.

"Spunky!" Daphne's voice rang out. "Look, Peter, Spunky's swimming."

Peter reached for me and lifted me onto his shoulders. I grabbed his neck and held on tightly, my heart pounding.

"Spunky loves the water as much as we

do," Daphne declared happily. Wrong as usual.

Peter swam back to shore with me around his neck. I could see Happy and Dodger prancing about anxiously. When we reached the shallow water, I jumped off Peter and swam toward them. They bounded over to me, eyes full of wonder. I shook myself vigorously, and the cold water sprayed them like pellets. They yelped and jumped away from me. But they had to come back to sniff me up and down. Each time they came close, I shook some more water off my coat, making them yelp and jump back. That was much more fun than the swimming.

16

What made everything change? Some things happened slowly and at first did not seem very important. But when things changed, they changed so quickly I was bewildered.

First there were differences in Daphne. Her familiar quick footsteps around the house became more and more of a shuffling sound. Some days she became weary in the middle of cleaning or preparing dinner and had to go to bed. Those evenings Peter had to fill our bowls, and there were no treats to be had from Daphne's cooking pots.

At night, the conversation between Peter and Daphne seemed to center around a new word — baby. From the sound of their voices, it seemed to be something very special. I wondered what a baby was like.

They also talked more and more about Dodger's hives. At least they kept wondering if it was hives. Dodger had developed a lump on one side of her face, and although she didn't whimper about it, the lump seemed to be growing bigger and bigger.

One day Peter came home early to take Dodger to see the "nice" doctor. It was one of Daphne's bad days and Peter made her stay home with us. Happy and I ran to the stone ledge to watch them drive away. We could see Dodger's head sticking out of the side window, looking back at us. And that was the last time we saw Dodger.

When Peter returned he was alone. Instead of rubbing our heads the way he usually did when he came home, he just trudged into the house without even looking at either one of us. We followed him inside.

When Daphne saw Peter, the look of alarm on her face made me stand perfectly still. She was at the kitchen sink, her hands dripping with soapy water. Peter put his arms around her and made her sit down in a chair.

"It's cancer," he said quietly. "The doctor is operating now. He'll call us as soon as it's over."

Daphne took a quick breath and pressed her knuckles against her mouth. Peter brought her a glass of water and made her take a few sips. Then he sat down next to her and they huddled over the kitchen table talking quietly. I stretched out under the table near their feet, filled with the sadness in their voices.

When the phone rang, Daphne jumped up to grab it, overturning her chair as she moved. Then she simply handed the phone to Peter, without speaking into it.

Peter cleared his throat. "Hullo. Yes . . . Yes, I see . . . I see. You did all you could. Yes, it's better that way." His voice was low, almost a whisper. He put the phone back in place.

"Dodger's gone," he said.

Daphne sobbed in Peter's arms for a long time.

Dodger was gone. I waited and looked for her, but she did not come back. The house seemed empty without her. The fields stretched endlessly, and the terrace became a barren, stricken place. Sometimes I visited the tree with the hollow in it, wishing she were still there. Each time I came home from my wanderings, I expected to find that anxious head ready to sniff me up and down to make sure I was all right. But she wasn't there.

I missed her. A dull pain throbbed inside me each time I found traces of her scent in the den, in the comfortable nooks of the terrace, in the kitchen, near the fireplace, in her empty bowl.

All I could do was wait. I had learned how to wait. In the meantime, I found myself doing the things she did: barking at the milkman and the mailman, keeping a watchful eye on Peter and Daphne and Happy, staying close to the house.

Her bowl remained on the terrace outside. Some days it filled with rain water. When it dried a film of dust settled on the bottom, but Daphne did not take it away.

17

"Peter, are you sure we're making the right decision?" Peter and Daphne were talking in the kitchen after dinner.

"It's the only sensible thing to do," Peter said. "You'll have the best of care, and the baby will have a lot of relatives to grow up with."

"My sister says we can stay with her as long as we have to, until we get settled." Daphne's voice was low.

"That won't take us long. The main thing is making sure you've got a good doctor."

Daphne bit her thumbnail.

"You know," Peter said brightly, "I think

I'll like the idea of having snow in the winter. I've lived in southern California all my life."

"It's almost summertime there now. You'll have to have a little patience."

"It will be easier to move in warm weather."

"Peter, how on earth will we manage?"

"I'll finish this job in a couple of weeks. All you have to do is get on a plane, straight to your sister's house. We can sell whatever we don't want to take along. I'll pile the rest into a truck and drive there in a week."

"Clear across the country? With Spunky and Happy?"

"Sure. We'll manage just fine. There's nothing to worry about."

"I hate the thought of moving, Peter. We've been so happy here."

"We'll be happy there too. Besides, we'll have the baby."

What was a baby like? And how would Dodger ever find us again if we moved away?

Strange people began coming to our house. I barked ferociously at each new arrival. But once inside the house, these strangers stroked me and said nice things about me, and I just stayed around them out of curiosity. Some of them took pieces of furniture away with them, and the house became more barren-looking with each visit.

One afternoon Daphne took all of her clothes out of the closet and folded them into suitcases. Happy and I watched her with a feeling of apprehension. When she was finished, she snapped the cases shut. Her things were locked inside. The next morning Peter carried the cases to the back of the car and closed the raised lid over them.

Daphne was leaving us. We followed her outside, not knowing what to do. We pressed close to her legs as she walked. When she got to the car, she looked down at us, and gave us a familiar command.

"Stay and be good dogs," she said. Her voice was quivering. She knelt down and hugged us both. I choked back a whimper and looked into her eyes.

"We'll be together soon," she said, then bit her lips.

Slowly she got up and climbed inside the car. Peter started the motor, and Daphne gazed at us from the side window. Tears were running down her cheeks.

As they drove away, we chased after the car until it turned off our property onto the paved road. Then we ran back to the house and jumped onto the stone ledge to keep watch.

It was hours before Peter returned. Instead of the familiar car, he was driving a small truck. At first we barked and barked at it until we saw him behind the wheel. When he got out, he cheerfully rubbed our heads, but Daphne was not with him.

We followed him inside the house. Large cartons sat awkwardly in the middle of the living room, filled with our belongings. An armchair and couch were the only pieces of furniture left in the room.

Peter carried some of the cartons to the truck and put them inside. We followed his every move and often got under his feet, but he didn't lose patience with us. Peter never did.

Later that evening, he filled our bowls with nuggets, and then slumped into the armchair and fell asleep. There was no gravy from Daphne's pot, and no after-dinner biscuit. I scratched the side of Peter's chair to remind him, but could not wake him up.

The house was chilly, and Happy and I huddled next to Peter's feet to keep warm. When the sun rose, Peter woke as cheerful as ever. He loaded the rest of the cartons into the truck, then locked the doors of the house. After inspecting the truck from all angles, he whistled for us to jump in. Then he got in beside us.

We drove slowly down the side road. It felt good to be going somewhere. We passed the fields alongside the dirt road. I took a last look at Dodger's old tree. I stuck my head out the window as far as possible and looked back. The house was growing smaller and smaller against my mountains and had already closed its eyes.

It was raining, and the steady thump, thump of the windshield wipers lulled me to sleep. I woke up when Peter pulled alongside a building with brightly lit windows all around it. We got out and I stretched luxuriously, enjoying the feel of the ground and the crisp air. The rain had stopped, leaving a fresh, fragrant scent over the leaves and grass.

Happy ran about wildly, first in circles, then darting in and out of the half-open door we were heading toward. I kept close to Peter, making sure I didn't lose him in these strange surroundings. A man behind a desk gave Peter a key and we went outside again. There were rows of doors all alike. Peter fit the key into one door and we went inside.

It was a small, stuffy room. Strange smells hit my nostrils the moment we entered. Over layers of human odors hung the sharp, penetrating vapor of disinfectant. I did not like being in this room.

Peter filled two cups of water for Happy and me and then flung himself on the bed. In less than a minute he was asleep. Happy and I curled up together on a fuzzy, soft rug in the bathroom and fell into an uneasy sleep. Who did this room belong to? Which one of the strangers who had left his scent behind would return to claim it?

All night long I could hear sounds through the walls: Cars screeched by, there was whispered talk, a loud, high laugh, wind hissing through the trees. But the door was closed and I could not get out to investigate.

At last Peter awoke. After washing himself, he led us outside to the truck. I watched the sun come up as we drove away.

It was clear to me that our normal times for eating and sleeping were over. I thought of the meat and gravy Daphne served us over crisp nuggets, and my stomach ached. I patted Peter's arm to get his attention. I had to make him understand. He looked at me, and I grunted.

"What do you want?" he asked with a smile.

I repeated my grunt, this time snapping my jaws together and shifting my front paws for emphasis.

"You want to eat?"

I sneezed loudly, the closest sound I could make for "yes."

"It won't be long, Spunky." He pulled up to a little building at the side of the road, where pungent smells of food made us drool. Peter brought us round flat chunks of fried meat, hot and crisp at the edges. We devoured them.

We drove all that day, and when we stopped to eat that night I sniffed something very familiar. It was the heavy smoke of charcoal, the same smell we used to have on our terrace when Peter cooked outside. I sniffed the air anxiously. Would Daphne be here? Dodger? No, there was no trace of them.

When Peter handed me a piece of charcoaled meat, I turned my head away.

"What's the matter, Spunky?" There was genuine alarm in his voice.

I stared straight ahead, keeping my mouth tightly shut. I had no appetite at that moment.

18

We had been traveling for several days, and Happy was growing more and more restless. Each time Peter stopped and let him out, he ran wild. When Peter was ready to move on, he whistled for Happy to come. After a few moments of waiting, that crazy pup raced up, but each day we had to wait longer and longer.

One evening we were parked in front of a highway restaurant where Peter had gone in to eat. He brought us our dinner on a plastic dish — bits of meat, fish, and cooked vegetables. After eating this delicious meal, Happy and I decided to stretch our legs.

But instead of coming back to the truck with me after our run, Happy kept going.

Peter whistled for some time, but Happy was nowhere in sight. We walked around to the back of the restaurant where there were several tall garbage cans. Happy's head peered out at us, then ducked back.

Peter ran after him, but Happy scooted right past us, and disappeared before we could turn around.

Time passed. Peter sat down next to the garbage cans with me beside him, waiting for Happy to shoot by us again. Peter's back rested against the building, his feet bent up under his chin. I could see he was tired. His eyes were blinking sleepily, and from time to time he shook his head to keep awake.

There he was! Peter lunged, but Happy darted right past us. I was tempted to chase him, but didn't want to leave Peter's side.

Suddenly a shadow fell over us, blotting out the light from the restaurant.

"Lose something, mister?" A huge man with a rough edge to his voice loomed over us. Bright metal gleamed on his jacket and cap. I stood rigid. Men who wore caps that hid their eyes were not to be trusted.

Peter stood up, brushing the dirt from his clothes.

"My dog, officer. I lost my dog."

"Oh, you lost your dog. Seems to me you've got him right there at your feet."

"Not that dog, officer, another one. Happy — his name's Happy." Peter crouched down again: "Here, Happy. Here, Happy."

At that moment Happy came darting by, brushing Peter's trousers and making the officer step back quickly.

Peter flung his arm out to catch that slippery black body, but his arm fell with an empty thud to his side.

The officer knelt down. "Here, Happy, Happy. Over here."

He was gone again. The officer straightened up and took a shiny metal whistle out of his pocket.

"This will get him." He blew shrill, long shrieks through the air. Happy's head poked out from the corner of the building. The officer backed away a few steps, blowing the whistle. Happy came closer, fascinated. He trotted toward us.

The officer squatted down beside the garbage can and blew short, soft whistles. When Happy was almost in front of him, the officer made the grab. His hand came up with a juicy watermelon rind. Happy was right behind him.

The officer straightened up and shoved his cap to the back of his head. I noticed with surprise that his eyes were not unkind.

"Good luck, mister," he said, and slowly walked away.

Happy was nowhere to be seen again. Peter went back to the truck, motioned me to get in, and we started to drive away.

Where was Happy? I leaned out the window and looked back. There he was, coming after us as fast as his legs could go.

Peter was watching in the side mirror. Happy was losing ground, trailing far behind us. At last Peter stopped the truck. Up the road came Happy, panting and gasping, but still at a good trot.

Only when he was right in front of us, tongue hanging loosely out of the side of his mouth, did Peter bend down and pick him up. Once inside the truck, Happy curled up beside me and fell asleep. He had that silly grin on his face.

The next morning we were at a gasoline station on the highway. Cars were coming and going in every direction. A man in overalls had pumped gas into the truck, and now Peter was checking the tires.

Happy and I watched all the activity on the highway from the side window. A small boy was leaning against one of the gas pumps staring at us. My ears pricked up when I saw him, and I cocked my head to one side. He smiled and I could tell he wanted to pet me. Sure enough, he came over to the truck and tried to reach me. He gripped the door handle to pull himself up. With a click, the door fell open and Happy darted out.

The next minute there was a piercing screech of car brakes and a horrible yelp that blotted out all the other sounds. Then everyone was running. I jumped out of the truck as Peter ran past me. I followed close on his heels. We reached a crowd of people standing around a car that was half on and half off the highway.

Peter elbowed his way through the circle of people. But their feet quickly moved together, locking me out. I could only catch glimpses of what was going on.

"That your dog, mister?"

"Yes, it is." Peter's voice was strangled in his throat.

The man was wiping his face with a large handkerchief. "Sure am sorry," he said. "Just didn't see him."

The feet in front of me were shifting and I quickly squeezed in between them. Peter was kneeling down and touching a dark form on the ground. It was Happy. He didn't move. I started to whimper, and Peter scooped me off the ground and carried me through the crowd. He put me inside the truck and closed the door.

I pressed my nose against the window, trying to see what I could. A car with blinding lights circling around its top pulled up, and men with caps on their heads got out. I saw Peter walk toward them. He was carrying Happy in his arms. He spoke with them for a few moments, then he got into their car, still holding Happy. They drove off, and the crowd of people melted away.

I waited. A dull, throbbing ache welled up inside my chest, making my ears pound. After a long time, Peter came back and got in the truck beside me. He put the key in the slot and started the motor. Then he reached out and touched my head.

"No more Happy," he said.

No more Happy? Would I never have

Happy again? Or was it only for a little while? I swallowed back the thumping inside me, and tried hard to understand. I moved close to Peter, pressing up against his side. His nearness gave me comfort.

19

We kept on. Driving. Eating. Sleeping.
It rained more often now. My paws were
covered with dried mud and my shaggy hair
was matted with knots. Daphne had not
brushed me in a long time. Daphne?

Sometimes the sweet smell of fresh cut
grass or sights of animals dotting the curve
of sloping hills stirred my interest as we
drove along.

Once I saw two dogs running along the
edge of the road, heading toward us. One
was big, the other small. I scrambled to the
side window and leaned out as far as I
could. Dodger? Happy? The truck swept past
them, and I saw they were just a couple of

strange dogs. Still, I watched them disappear down the road until I could no longer see their tails swaying behind them.

I settled back in my seat and stared straight ahead. The thumping ache inside had become a familiar part of me now.

The scenery was changing. More houses appeared along the road, some of them stretching high up into the sky. More cars followed or passed us.

"We're almost there!" Peter said. For the first time since we'd lost Happy, he turned and smiled at me.

We left the highway and drove along quiet streets lined with thick, tall trees. At one street we slowed down, and Peter searched the houses, one by one. He stopped in front of a house surrounded by neatly cut grass and big sprawling trees.

"This is it," Peter said. "Come on, Spunk."

We got out, and I rolled on the sweet-smelling grass while Peter pushed the doorbell.

A woman opened the door and threw her arms around him. It was not Daphne. I slipped through the open door into the house. A little girl jumped back when she saw me.

"Oh, Mommy," she cried. "This dog is dirty!"

The woman called "Mommy" did not look at me. She was completely absorbed in Peter.

"Oh, Peter," she was saying, "Daphne's in the hospital." Her hand was clasped on his arm.

"What's wrong?" Peter's voice was shaky.

"She's been there since yesterday. It seems the baby is arriving much sooner than we thought."

"I'll go to her right away."

"I'll take you there, Peter. It's not very far."

They walked to the door, and I pressed myself against it, ready to go with them.

Peter looked down at me.

"You stay." Then to the little girl he said, "Take good care of Spunky, will you?"

The woman opened the door and took Peter's arm.

"Don't worry," she said cheerfully. "The dog will be all right. It's a very quiet neighborhood. We have a cat, you know, Princess. She's very shy, the little dear. Hides when strangers are in the house."

"Spunk will behave herself."

"I'm sure there'll be no trouble."

The door closed and Peter was gone. I

was alone with the little girl. I gently wagged my tail at her. Her stiffly pleated skirt swayed as she backed away from me.

"You sure are dirty," she said.

The little girl walked to the back door and opened it. I went outside.

For a moment, I didn't know where to go. Where was Peter? Where was everything I used to know so well? The sun was bright and the bushes and grass had strange new smells. There were trees and flowers behind the house. I was soon absorbed in sniffing each one of them to learn all I could about my new surroundings.

There was a rustling in the tree above me, and I looked up. A cat was sitting on one of the branches, staring down at me. My heart leaped, but I did not move or bark. Our eyes locked. "No more cats for me," I remembered painfully.

I lowered my gaze and walked away. I paused in front of a nearby bush and sniffed intently. The cat backed down the tree, then sharpened its claws on the bark. The sound made me wince, but I pretended not to hear. I continued sniffing. She sat at the foot of the tree, waiting.

I had to prove she did not scare me. I moved about slowly, pausing to examine everything in my path. Time passed and my courage grew. I geared myself for the next step I was going to take.

Without moving my head or eyes, I strolled past the cat as if she wasn't there. Her body stiffened tightly as I went by, but she didn't lunge.

"Princess! Here Princess!" It was the little girl at the back door, holding it open.

The cat darted into the doorway and vanished inside the house. The little girl closed the door quickly.

I was shocked. The cat called Princess lived in this house. It was hers, not mine. I shook myself vigorously to rid myself of the prickly feeling down my spine.

For some time I searched the neighborhood for scraps of food but, except for one broken bit of stale bread near a garbage can, could find nothing. The sun was going down, and hunger gripped my stomach.

"Spunky! Spunky!" My ears pricked up. It was the little girl. Her voice sounded far away, but I knew where to go. In a few minutes I was back at the house. She was waiting in front of it, and clapped her hands when she saw me.

"Time for dinner. Come on."

Dinner! They were going to feed me.

She held the door open and I ran into the kitchen, but stopped short at the sight. There was Princess, hunched over a bowl of food. She hesitated for a moment, then darted out of the room. Hah! I liked that! Within a few seconds I ate all the tiny nuggets in her bowl.

"That's not your dinner!" the little girl scolded. She spooned hunks of meat out of a can and put it down for me.

Delicious!

While I ate, she poured more nuggets into the cat's bowl and placed it on the floor near me. Where was the cat? Somehow I could feel her presence again in the room. I looked around carefully. There she was! Crouched on top of the sink, watching me eat!

I could not let her know how uncomfortable she made me feel. I continued to eat, as slowly as possible.

When I finished, I walked away a few paces and sprawled down on the floor. I rested my chin on my paw and waited.

The cat jumped down and slunk over to her bowl. She did not eat, but darted her eyes at me. I turned my head away and pretended to sleep.

She took a small bite of her food. I yawned and stretched out. The movement made her scamper out of the room. Hah! I could frighten her easily. I rolled on my back and pawed the air, tingling with pleasure. Then I got up and cleaned out her bowl again. She would have to learn that any leftovers were mine, even though this was her house!

Later that evening, Peter returned with the woman. I jumped up and ran to greet him, wagging my tail, but he only touched my head with his hand.

I followed Peter and the woman into the kitchen. He slumped into a chair and rubbed his eyes, while the woman fussed with pots and pans.

"Daphne seems so weak," he said. "I never thought she would give birth so soon."

"Please don't worry, Peter. My sister is a strong girl, you know." There was a forced cheerfulness in her voice.

"I hope the baby will be all right," Peter said, half to himself. There was that word baby again.

"You'll have a fine baby, you'll see."

They talked on and on. I sat down on top of Peter's foot. He stroked my head without looking at me. At least I had him near me now.

For several days, it was the same. Peter returned to the house each evening and spoke to the woman about Daphne and the baby. I sat at his feet listening to the worried sound of his voice.

During these days, I wandered about outside, sniffing and searching. Although I was well-fed, there was a longing inside me that felt very much like hunger. The longing, strangely enough, was to be held tightly in someone's arms. Yes, Daphne's arms.

I stayed close to the house most of the time, hoping Peter would suddenly return. But only Princess kept showing up. Each time I spotted her peeking out from under a bush and staring down at me from a tree, my spine twinged in alarm. She was watching me, but I kept pretending not to see her, reminding myself that I could scare her easily if I wanted to.

Early this morning, when I was let outside, I found Princess crouched low in the grass just a few feet in front of me. I sprawled down flat, facing her, leaving a safe distance between us, my chin between my paws.

Our eyes locked. I kept perfectly still. So did she. The hair falling over my eyes shaded me somewhat from the brightness of her glare. Her spine hairs were standing straight up, but she did not blink.

We stayed this way for a long time, testing each other's control. Now I decided it was time to scare her. I sat up quickly and vigorously scratched my ear, anxious to see her dart away.

No, she only sat up too. Her spine hairs were soft and smooth. She blinked her eyes contentedly and began to wash one of her paws. I got up and casually strolled away, trying to hide my disappointment. Princess was no longer afraid of me.

A few streets away, I followed an inviting pathway leading to the top of a hill. Suddenly a dog came bounding across the top and stood rigidly against the sky. The sunlight blinded me for an instant. The dog was powerful and slender, with long, flowing ears like — Dodger! *Was it Dodger?* I galloped up to it, my heart pounding with joy.

But the moment I reached the dog, I realized it was not Dodger. The strange dog snarled down at me, baring its fangs. I turned away and slowly trotted down the hill. The dog leaped after me and sank its teeth into my back.

I cried out in pain and twisted away, running down the hill as fast as I could. I ran all the way back to the house. The front and back doors were closed. I looked around for a place to hide.

There was a car parked in front of the house and I crawled underneath it. Pain flooded through me.

I sank down on the cold, greasy pavement. Now the pain of my wound seem to mingle with all the aching sadness I had felt inside me for so many days. I whimpered and shuddered for a long time, until an odd tiredness came over me.

I remained still, flattened against the pavement. I had no desire to move, to go anywhere.

A shadow flickered across the pavement. Crouching underneath the curve of a tire was Princess. She was staring at me. I turned my head to avoid her glaring eyes. Was she going to lunge at me and pierce me with her sharp claws? If she did I still wouldn't move or run away. There was a numbness to my pain now, and nothing more could add to it.

I glanced at her again. She moved toward me, tail curling above her head, eyes flashing their light. She came closer and closer, until she was standing hunched up over my head. I searched her eyes, wondering vaguely when she would strike.

She crouched down in front of me, her whiskers just a breath away from my face. Her eyes blinked, and then she brushed her nose against mine and quickly darted away. It was a kiss. Princess had kissed me. The wonder of it startled me for a moment. Princess was my friend. But the wonder soon melted into the sadness and settled beside my pain. Nothing mattered anymore.

Time passed. I did not stir even when I heard a car stop in front of the house. I heard Peter's voice and footsteps. He was with someone.

They were going inside the house. I recognized the footsteps of the person with him. Was it . . . ?

"It's so good to be home, Peter."

Daphne? I was afraid to be mistaken. I raised my head and listened carefully. They were at the door now, and other voices mixed with theirs.

They were inside the house. Was it really Daphne?

I crawled out from under the car and

tottered to the front door. I scratched it with my paw. Would they hear me? No one came to open it.

I went around the back. Closed. There were some windows I could see through if I stood on my hind legs. I tried one window after another. I had a fleeting glimpse of the back of Peter's head, but no Daphne. I kept trying, balancing myself on my hind legs, stretching my neck backward and standing far enough away from the window to catch the right angle. Another window. Then I saw her. She had her head to one side and was looking down at a bundle she was cradling in her arms. There was a smile on her lips.

I held my breath. She was moving toward me now, and lowering the bundle into a small, high bed close to the window. Daphne raised her head and I saw her face fully. Her eyes suddenly flew apart.

"Spunky!" she cried.

I wagged my tail slowly.

In another moment Daphne was standing at the back door, holding it wide open. I ran to her. She knelt down and pulled me into her arms, hugging me tightly. How good it was to feel her warmth, her love seeping through me, to breathe her scent again.

Inside the hallway, she examined me more closely.

"Oh, Spunky," she gasped when she saw my wound. "What happened to you?" She hurried to get some medicine, and then spread it on my back. She was kneeling close beside me. Her hands were soothing; the medicine was cool.

I no longer felt dazed. Daphne was home.

"Come with me, Spunk!" she commanded.

I followed her into a bedroom. She walked to the high bed and gently lifted something out. It was covered with blankets.

She settled herself into a chair that rocked back and forth. I sat down next to it and watched her intently.

She leaned toward me, stopping the movement of the chair. With one hand, she parted the blankets.

A small head appeared. It was yawning.

"Say hello to the baby, Spunk," she said softly.

So this was a baby!

Daphne smoothed back the hairs falling over my eyes. I turned my head and kissed her hand. Then I reached up and kissed the baby's face.

That was the first time I saw you.

You are so small, and I know I will have to take care of you.

ABOUT THE AUTHOR

John Updike was born in Shillington, Pennsylvania. He is a graduate of Harvard College and a Knox Fellow of the Ruskin School of Design and Fine Arts, Oxford. He lives in Beverly Farms, Massachusetts.

He is the author of fourteen novels and several collections of short stories. He won the Pulitzer Prize, the American Book Award, and the National Book Critics Circle Award for RABBIT IS RICH. Fawcett has published and continues to publish most of his work.

His is the author of ten collections of short stories, including two volumes of linked tales, BECH: A BOOK and BECH IS BACK.